D1285818

FORMS and YOU

Revised Edition

Edited by Nadine B. Stukel
Revised with assistance from Debra Kaufman

J. Weston Walch, Publisher
Portland, Maine

2   3   4   5   6   7   8   9   10

ISBN 0-8251-0141-7

Copyright © 1983
J. Weston Walch, Publisher
P.O. Box 658 • Portland, Maine 04104-0658

Printed in the United States of America

Contents

Introduction

American life sometimes seems to be built around forms. Therefore, this set of masters should help students get a good start in life. The set covers so many different aspects of life that it will be useful in many classes — business, social studies, home economics, and English. It will probably be most useful in English classes, for there it will serve a triple purpose — giving students practice in filling out forms, familiarizing them with reading and following directions, and helping them learn to write concise, meaningful answers. Finally, the set will also prove useful to guidance counselors seeking to acquaint students with life beyond the walls of the school.

These masters will provide hundreds of clean, legible copies. We recommend that students actually fill out most of the forms to the best of their ability. In the process, they may well realize how many details of their lives are already beyond the fringes of memory. Use of the set should help convince them to start keeping detailed records of their personal histories.

One note of caution is in order. Some of the forms call for quite personal information. We recommend that you tell students to omit any such facts that they prefer not to divulge. Teachers should make clear that the forms are being used to give students useful experience, not to pry. This is one reason why questions on drug and sex experience have been omitted from the armed forces application. However, these sections are included in the notes "To the Teacher" and can be shown to the class on an overhead projector for general discussion. In other instances where forms have been shortened, the reasons are to save space and to avoid duplication among the forms.

Of course, the ages and backgrounds of students using these forms will vary considerably. While some students will have a lot of real information to use in the forms, others will have to create fictitious information. In the latter case, many teachers will prefer to have individual students use their imaginations; other teachers will provide information for everyone in the class to use. An example of such information is given on page xiv for Masters 33 through 35.

—Nadine B. Stukel and
Debra Kaufman

To the Teacher

These notes include a list and explanation of the forms in this package, suggestions for class vocabulary work, and some suggested student activities.

1. SOCIAL SECURITY FORM

Master 1 is the form students use to apply for a Social Security card when they are sixteen years old. This card makes students eligible for all forms of Social Security benefits. (These benefits are described in detail in most encyclopedias and almanacs.) Students should be encouraged to fill out this form when they become eligible, and to make changes at the appropriate times. They may obtain actual copies of this application form at the county courthouse or the nearest Social Security office. Applicants must provide evidence of age, identity, and citizenship by submitting the appropriate documents.

ACTIVITIES

1. Have a speaker from the Social Security office explain benefits and eligibility requirements, answer questions, and provide a brief history of the development of Social Security.

2. Have a panel discussion or a debate, or assign a written report discussing the adequacy of our Social Security system. Encourage students to interview Social Security personnel and recipients as well as to find articles on the subject.

2. PROMISE OF VACATION EMPLOYMENT

This form is an application for a work permit that must be obtained by minors who are still in school and wish to work. The employer fills out the form; the minor and his or her parent or guardian must sign it. The minor must come in person to sign the work permit, and must bring either a birth certificate or driver's license as proof of age. If the application is approved, a certificate is issued by the U.S. Department of Labor's Bureau of Standards to children from fourteen to seventeen years of age. The certificate protects minors against employment that might be unsuitable to their age, health, and ability. It also protects the employer from unknowingly violating the law by hiring persons who have lied about their age.

VOCABULARY

affidavit — sworn statement in writing
documentary — proved by written records
prospective — expected
stipulations — conditions or requirements

ACTIVITIES

1. Have students research and report on the child labor laws of 1916, 1919, and 1924, which were challenged and declared unconstitutional.

2. Have students research and report on the Fair Labor Standards Act of 1938, which established the basic standards for child labor.

3. Ask students to investigate why certain occupations (such as agricultural work) are exempt from minimum wage laws for minors. Why are some occupations prohibited for minors? Have the students discuss the fairness of these exclusions.

4. Have a lawyer or Bureau of Employment employee who is knowledgeable about the above laws speak to the class.

3. UNEMPLOYMENT COMPENSATION INSURANCE CLAIM

Unemployment compensation insurance is paid for by employers, who contribute to state funds to protect unemployed workers. When a worker has been "laid off" or dismissed unfairly from a job, he or she may be eligible to collect a weekly check from the government. In most states, a person who has quit a job or who was fired for "just cause" cannot collect these benefits.

VOCABULARY

fraud penalties — punishment fixed by law (i.e., fine or imprisonment) for a false statement of claim
severance pay — money given to a worker who has been dismissed from a job

ACTIVITIES

1. Ask students to investigate the employment security laws in their state and find out the eligibility requirements. Then have a claims representative from the state employment agency explain her or his job to the class.

2. Ask students to research the history of the establishment of the Employment Security Commission, or ask a knowledgeable historian to explain the commission's origins.

4-8. DRIVING FORMS

These forms are for various driving privileges: operator's license, vehicle title, and international permit, plus making necessary changes. Further information about each form may be obtained from your local AAA office, driver training personnel, or public safety department. These forms vary from state to state, but the basic information required is the same.

VOCABULARY

consent — permission
duplicate — an exact copy
husbandry — farming
in loco parentis — in the place of a parent
lien — an interest in property to secure a debt
mandatory — required
notarized — signed by a notary public who vouches for your
    signature
revoked — taken away indefinitely
suspended — taken away for a given period of time

ACTIVITIES

1. Have students research and report on your state's laws concerning driving, including when the first driving tests were given and what these tests involved.

2. Have a motor club official or public safety officer speak to the class about driving and the law.

9. COLLEGE BOARD ADMISSION TESTING APPLICATION (SAT)

This is the application form students must fill out in order to take the college entrance examination. An incorrectly filled out form may hold up a student's admission to college. The school guidance counselor is a good source of additional information about this form. For activities, see 10-11 following.

10, 11. COLLEGE ADMISSION APPLICATION

The student fills out this form in order to be admitted to college. The form in this package is for a small state college. It will serve as an example of the information usually required. A nonrefundable fee must accompany this application. Students must also see that their high school transcripts and SAT or ACT scores are sent to the college admissions office. Application forms from nearby colleges and universities may be obtained to offer a more complete sampling.

ACTIVITY (for both college-related forms)

Invite a guidance counselor or college admissions person to visit the class. This person can explain the importance of the various forms, how they are evaluated, common errors, and other items of interest. This should be done before college-bound students actually fill out these forms in order to prepare them to handle the forms successfully.

12. FORMS FOR SAVINGS AND CHECKING ACCOUNTS

A. Checking Account Application

This form is used to open a checking account if the bank accepts the account. A checking account provides a safe place to keep money, a faster way to pay bills (by mail instead of by personal delivery), and a record of what has been spent and deposited. Once the bank accepts the application, an account number is assigned.

VOCABULARY

account number — a number given to the account holder and put on the holder's checks and deposit slips as a means of identification

title of account — your name, or names if the account is joint

survivor — person entitled to the balance of money in your account if you should die

depositor — person entitled to put money into the account

initial deposit — first sum of money put into the account (some banks require a certain amount)

B. Savings Account Application

This form will entitle the applicant to save money and to earn interest on an account. Savings add up fast if deposits are made regularly. The student may withdraw money when it is needed or may transfer money to his or her checking account. However, stress that the primary advantage of a savings account is to save money long enough to earn interest on it.

C-D. Checks and Deposit Slips

These forms are used after the student opens a checking account. Emphasize the importance of keeping accurate records of the money put into the account and taken from the account. Explain that personal checking account records may determine future business with the bank and other institutions. Deposit slips show the date and amount of money put into the account. The student writes a check when he or she wishes to pay for something. The checkbook has a place to keep a record of deposits and checks written.

VOCABULARY

> endorse — to sign your name on the back of a check made out to you
>
> balance — amount of money remaining in your account after you write a check

ACTIVITY

You can offer students the opportunity to fill out more than one check. Practice in keeping a checking account can be done with worksheets. You can make up situations in which the student writes various checks, receives a bank statement, and reconciles the account.

13-15. LOAN APPLICATIONS

Inform students that once they have demonstrated their ability to handle checking and savings accounts, they may be eligible to borrow money from the bank. The direct loan application (Master 13) will allow students to borrow money for personal use. The residential loan application (Masters 14 and 15) is for funds for buying a home. The amount students may borrow for this purpose depends on the down payment, personal income, and the value of the home they are buying. Most banks have pamphlets for their customers that explain the bank's services in more detail.

VOCABULARY

> assets — anything owned that has exchange value
>
> credit reference — someone who will say that you have paid your debts
>
> dividends — money received from securities (bonds, insurance)
>
> escrow impounds — additional expenses such as taxes and insurance that you may wish to include in your loan payments
>
> interest — charge you pay for borrowing money
>
> liabilities — debts you have not paid; amounts owed
>
> principal — amount of money borrowed
>
> spouse — husband or wife

ACTIVITIES

1. Have a qualified bank employee speak to the class about various bank services and answer questions that students have. This may work better after some class work with the forms.

2. Invite a lawyer to explain your state's laws about property shared by husband and wife.

16. CREDIT CARD APPLICATIONS

A credit card allows the buyer to buy now and pay later. An application for a credit card helps the company that is issuing the card to determine if an applicant is a good credit risk. Students should be made aware of the importance of establishing a good credit rating. They should know that some credit cards are widely accepted (MasterCard and Visa, *A*) and some credit cards can be used only for gasoline or in a particular department store (*B*). All companies have a finance charge, dependent upon interest rates, for the privilege of using their credit cards. Students also should know that if they consistently buy above their ability to pay, they will lose their credit. Credit information is kept on everyone throughout the country who has ever had credit. These files are available to credit holders who wish to see them.

VOCABULARY

account number — a number assigned to the cardholder for identification purposes
authorized — done with permission
finance charges — money charged for borrowing money and paying it back in installments

ACTIVITIES

1. Have a class discussion on how to establish a good credit rating.
2. Have someone from a bank, store, or credit bureau speak to the class about credit abuse. (Major credit card applications may be obtained from banks.)
3. Have students interview several store managers whose stores offer credit and report to the class.

17. FORD MOTOR CREDIT COMPANY CUSTOMER STATEMENT

This loan application or one from any major automobile manufacturer is considered a customer service for the car buyer. The loan is made with the automobile company instead of with a local banking service.

18. CREDIT UNION APPLICATIONS

A credit union is a cooperative savings and loan association operated by its members, who pool their savings. Credit unions are usually formed by employees of companies or members of educational, religious, and social institutions. The amount invested can be deducted from earnings through the payroll department. In addition to the savings and loan features, many credit unions have established a share draft account, which is similar to a bank's checking account.

Form A enables the applicant to put money into a credit union savings account. Form B is a credit union member's application for a credit union loan.

VOCABULARY

> beneficiary — person who will receive benefits of the accounts if the account holder dies
> comaker — someone who agrees to pay a loan if the applicant fails to
> dependents — people who depend on someone for support
> indemnify — to pay for loss or damage

ACTIVITY

> Have a member of a credit union or a qualified speaker from a credit union speak to the class about how credit unions function.

19. WITHHOLDING AND UNION FORMS

A. Employee's Withholding Allowance Certificate

The employee's withholding form tells the employer how many people depend on the employee for financial support. This information allows the employer to deduct the correct amount of income tax from the employee's salary.

VOCABULARY

> allowance — a share granted; each withholding allowance entitles a worker to have less tax withheld
> exemption — something that entitles the worker to pay less tax
> federal income tax — a tax, on money earned by working people, that helps finance our government
> perjury — lying under oath
> withholding — money taken from one's earnings for income taxes

B. Application for Union Membership

This application is used by workers who wish to join the union where they work. Unions give workers power to bargain for better wages and working conditions.

VOCABULARY

> collective bargaining — process of the union meeting with representatives from the company to gain benefits for its members
> designate — to name or specify
> dues — money paid regularly to belong to an organization
> grievance — a complaint against an unjust circumstance
> initiation fee or reinstatement fee — money paid to join an organization
> irrevocable — not capable of being taken back

ACTIVITIES

1. Have a local union representative speak to the class about the union and its benefits for the workers.

2. Ask someone knowledgeable about labor history to speak to the class on some aspect of the labor movement in the United States.

20-22. EMPLOYMENT APPLICATION

An employment application is the first impression an employer has of a job seeker, so it should be a good one. An incomplete or incorrectly filled out application may end up in the trash can. Application forms vary in how much information they want, but they all require certain basic information. Job applicants should have important dates and names and addresses of references written out so this information will be handy when they apply. Applications from several local places of employment may be collected to show how different industries and businesses vary their forms.

VOCABULARY

bond — insurance guaranteeing payment to an employer in case of financial loss caused by an employee

disposition — settlement

impairment or disability — any physical condition that might limit work performance (poor eyesight, weak back, and so on)

qualifications — education or experience that gives you the ability for a job

references — people who know you well enough to give accurate information about your personality and ability (always ask references for permission to use their names)

resumé — a short history of a person's job experience and qualifications

status — position or rank

termination — an ending or dismissal

ACTIVITIES

1. Have personnel department people from different types of companies speak to the class.

2. Visit factories and various places of business.

3. Ask an employment counselor or someone from the Equal Employment Opportunity Commission office to explain affirmative action and what kinds of employment interview practices are illegal.

23. APPLICATION FOR EMPLOYMENT—STATE BUREAU OF EMPLOYMENT SECURITY

If students wish their state bureau of employment security to assist them in finding jobs, they must fill out a form that gives information about themselves so that the bureau can evaluate their abilities. The bureau may also test applicants to find out what they are best suited to do.

ACTIVITY

Invite a representative from your state bureau of employment security to speak to the class about its services. He or she can explain about or even give a job evaluation test. Some schools do this on a yearly basis. If this is the case, you can plan to use this particular form at that time.

24. APPLICATION FOR CERTIFIED COPY OF BIRTH OR DEATH RECORD

If students cannot find their birth certificates, they should apply for copies. Proof of birth is necessary in many important cases: to obtain a driver's permit, to establish legal drinking age, to apply for jobs as a minor, to petition for naturalized citizenship, and so on. It is also necessary sometimes to have proof of death. This application can be obtained from the county courthouse, or by writing to the capital of the state where the person was born.

25. SELECTIVE SERVICE SYSTEM FORMS

All male citizens of the United States are required to register with the Selective Service System on their eighteenth birthday. (Although block 2 on the registration form has a box indicating "male" or "female," women are not required to register.) This registration is a prelude to actual induction into the armed services. The Privacy Act Statement, printed on the reverse side of both forms, is also shown on this spirit master, so that students may know to which agencies their information may be given. These forms may be obtained from and returned to the post office.

ACTIVITIES

1. Ask students to debate one or both of these questions:
    (a) The United States should reinstitute the draft; and/or
    (b) Women as well as men should be required to register for the Selective Service System.
2. Ask a knowledgeable army officer to speak to the class on the pros and cons of a volunteer army.

26-28. APPLICATION FOR ENLISTMENT — ARMED FORCES OF THE UNITED STATES

At the present time, one application form is used to apply for enlistment in the armed forces of the United States. This form requires much detail and can be obtained from the nearest recruiting office. Have the student check with the post office if he or she doesn't know where the recruiting office is located. In small cities the armed forces often work at post offices on certain days. A detailed instruction sheet comes with the application. Many students who want special training, but cannot afford the schooling, join the armed forces. The armed forces provide this training plus food, clothing, pay, and insurance. In order to join, a student must be a high school graduate. This form has been shortened, and the student should be given the information about the missing parts.

Part II. Examination and Enlistment Data Processing Codes — *for office use only* — on page 1 are omitted because they are not used by the applicant.

Part III. Number 27a, Previous Military Service, on page 2 is omitted because it is not filled in by the applicant.

Part IV. Numbers 37 through 41 are printed following these notes on page xxii. They can be used on an overhead projector and discussed so that students know what is asked, but they should not be filled out in class due to the personal nature of the information requested.

VOCABULARY

adjudication — a decision or sentence by a judge
certification — a written statement that something is true
civilian — one who is not in the armed services
component — a part of something
conscientious objector — one who refuses for moral or religious reasons to serve in the armed forces
dependents — people who rely on someone for support
derived citizenship — citizenship granted to a foreign-born child who becomes a citizen when his or her parents become citizens
naturalized citizen — foreign-born person who becomes a citizen
verification — proof that something is true

ACTIVITY

Have a recruiting officer speak to the class and answer questions.

29-32. APPLICATIONS FOR VARIOUS FORMS OF INSURANCE

People usually buy insurance to protect themselves from unexpected mishaps — accidents, surgery, fire, theft. Various kinds of insurance can help ease financial burdens. Insurance needs vary from person to person, so it is important to have an insurance representative you can trust. Applicants should get information from a reliable source on various insurance companies before they buy a policy.

VOCABULARY

annuity — an amount payable regularly or yearly

coverage — what your insurance will pay for

felony — a crime that can be punished by a jail term of more than one year

habitational — residential; used as a home

impairment — physical injury or handicap

lienholder — person with an interest in property to secure a debt

misdemeanor — a crime less serious than a felony

policy — written contract

premiums — money you pay for insurance

(revocable) beneficiary — person who receives the money if the insured person dies; if a beneficiary is revocable, the insured can name a new beneficiary at any time

(revocable) contingent beneficiary — person who receives the money if the first beneficiary is dead

ACTIVITIES

1.   Ask students to find consumer reports on several kinds of insurance and various individual insurance companies. Then have them compose pertinent questions that they would ask an insurance representative before buying a policy.

2.   Ask an insurance representative from each area of insurance to speak in a panel discussion for your class. (Students may want to use their questions from Activity 1 for this activity.)

33-35. TRAFFIC ACCIDENT REPORT AND SWORN STATEMENT IN PROOF OF LOSS

These reports could be used in conjunction with the insurance forms (perhaps as a mini-unit). The accident report is filled out by persons involved in a traffic accident when a police officer is not present; otherwise, the officer makes his or her own report. (This procedure will vary from state to state.)

Many students will enjoy using their imaginations to create the details required to fill in the forms. Some teachers will find it helpful, however, to provide information for student use. Here is the information developed for use with these forms by one teacher, Richard Greene of Roanoke Rapids, North Carolina:

Mr. John Smith of Roanoke Rapids, N.C., was in Commonweal, Pennsylvania, on a visit. The weather on Wednesday, June 7, 1978, was rainy as he traveled south on Gene Street. All of a sudden, he had to turn to the left to avoid hitting a pedestrian, Mary King. In the process, he hit an oncoming car being driven by Mary Tokas. Mr. Smith's car landed in Mr. Claude Homer's yard, damaging his fence. As a result of the mishap, Mr. Smith had to file an accident report in the state of Pennsylvania. Mr. Smith, whose address is 708 Roanoke Avenue, was driving a 1978 Ford LTD. His driver's license number was 3539-687980—vehicle license no. LSP 1789. He has insurance with Allstate Insurance Company—policy number 3384861—effective January 1978. The estimated damage to his car was $500.00. Mr. Smith hit Mary Tokas's 1978 Ford Pinto, resulting in $200.00 worth of damage. Her operator's license number was 836215 in the state of Pennsylvania. Mrs. Tokas's vehicle license number was JKL 6321 —also in Pennsylvania. She was born on June 9, 1944. She resides at 181 North Street in Commonweal. As her and Mr. Smith's cars collided, a pedestrian, Mrs. Mary King, was injured. She resides at 851 North Avenue in Commonweal. Property damage resulted with a broken fence belonging to Mr. Claude Homer of 761 Gene Street—damage estimated at $300.00. Mr. Smith reported that all of this happened at 1 P.M., a mile north of the intersection of Gene and South streets. Mr. Smith's accident was investigated by the Commonweal Police Department in the county of Merdex, Pennsylvania. Mr. Smith was born on August 4, 1935.

VOCABULARY

depreciation — a lowering from the original value of something
salvage — the use or value left in something

36. VOTER'S REGISTRATION

In order to exercise one's right to vote, a person first must register. Voter's registration forms vary from place to place, but require the same basic information. In order to register, one must be eighteen years of age. Some states require a person to be a resident of the state for a given number of days (usually thirty or sixty, but laws vary from state to state). A person can register at the county courthouse, or the city or town hall, or sometimes at other designated places.

VOCABULARY

elector — the voter
derivative naturalization — becoming a citizen because of one's
    parent's or spouse's citizenship
party affiliation — political party with which one is connected
    (for instance, Republican or Democratic)
personal naturalization — becoming a citizen on one's own
precinct — subdivision of a city (where one would vote)
registrar — person who registers voters
ward — subdivision of a city

ACTIVITIES

1. Ask students to study the Voting Rights Act and find out why it was introduced in the mid-1960's. A controversy arose in 1982 when this act was due for an extension. Have students read articles about the controversy and come prepared to class to discuss it.

2. A social science teacher could explain your state's voting procedures, or students could research the project themselves. You might start them out with some questions, such as: What does my vote do in a primary election? In a local election? If I move, how and when can I vote? What is an absentee ballot?

37. PASSPORT APPLICATION

If a student wishes to travel outside the United States, he or she will probably need a passport. Schools sometimes take students to foreign countries to enrich them and to promote better understanding between countries. The application for a passport can be obtained at the county courthouse, the post office, or through a reliable travel agency. Passport applications must be submitted with (1) proof of United States citizenship; (2) proof of identity; (3) two photographs; (4) passport and execution fees.

VOCABULARY

naturalized - became a citizen

ACTIVITIES

1. Ask students to find out what countries prohibit or restrict travel by their citizens. Discuss the political reasons for travel exchange, or lack of it, among countries.

2. Have students, teachers, or parents speak about traveling experiences.

38,39. MARRIAGE FORMS

Whether the wedding ceremony is performed by a clerical or secular person, everyone who plans to get married must get a marriage license. Laws pertaining to marriage vary from state to state, but most require a blood test, a license from the county or municipality, and a ceremony performed by a proper authority. When a minor wants to get married, he or she must have written (and notarized) permission from his or her parent or guardian.

VOCABULARY

notarized — signed by a notary public who vouches for your signature
officiant — the official performing an act or ceremony
ward — a person who is cared for by a guardian

ACTIVITIES

1. Have students research and report on their state's marriage laws.

2. Have students find out where they would obtain and file a marriage license in their area.

40, 41. APPLICATION FOR POST OFFICE BOX AND CHANGE-OF-ADDRESS FORMS

If the student wishes to receive mail at the post office, he or she should apply for a personal box. The post office has a form for this purpose. If the student moves, he or she should get change of address forms from the post office and notify those people, companies, magazines, and others who mail to the student. This will help avoid any delay in mail after the move.

42. APPLICATION FOR PLAN EXAMINATION AND BUILDING PERMIT

Whenever a person builds, adds on to, or repairs a building, a permit will probably be needed. Most towns and cities have zoning laws that specify certain building requirements. Applications are reviewed by the proper official and are either approved or rejected. A person may be fined if he or she does not obey these regulations.

VOCABULARY

ordinance — a law set forth by a governmental body, such as a city or county

zoning — the act of dividing an area into sections for specific uses, such as residence, business, manufacturing

ACTIVITIES

1. Have students find out if their city or town has any zoning ordinances, who issues the various permits, and what the fees are.

2. A debate may be possible if a local zoning dispute is taking place or has recently taken place; or an officer of the zoning board may speak to the class about zoning ordinances.

3. In small groups, have students create role-playing situations relating to zoning laws and/or building codes. (For example, a student may challenge the building codes enforcement officer on his or her plans for a house; a student may ask permission to install a composting toilet rather than the traditional kind; a farmer may want to build a "piggery" on his or her property.)

43. MAIL-ORDER FORMS

Explain to students that sometimes it is not convenient to go shopping. Catalogues allow people to buy from them without leaving home. Almost all magazines, as well as mail-order catalogues, sell something. If a person decides to buy, he or she must fill out the order blank. Encourage students to follow directions carefully, write neatly, and recheck the order. Mail-order houses lose a lot of money each year because of errors.

ACTIVITY

Ask the class to bring in various catalogues. Have them furnish a room, clothe children for school, or buy motorcycle parts, camping equipment, and other items. This is a good time to introduce consumer awareness. Have the class compare prices, brand names, and quality. Discuss budgets and dollar value. Perhaps you could have a contest to see who can do the best with the least money.

44. FEDERAL INCOME TAX, SHORT FORM 1040A

The federal government requires a portion of your income each year. This is called federal income tax. Most states and some cities also collect income taxes. If the student works, each year in early January he or she receives a booklet from the federal government that includes instructions and income tax forms. At the end of the year, the student's employer provides a W-2 form. This is a statement of earnings for the year; it also shows how much income tax was withheld for the year. Using this information and following the instructions in the booklet (teachers should obtain at least one copy of the current instructions), the student can fill out the income tax form. This form must be returned to the tax office by April 15. Some people who have large salaries and many complications let a qualified tax person do their forms for them. However, an average wage earner should be able to do his or her own form. Students should use the tax table, recheck, and remember to sign and date the form.

VOCABULARY

compensation — payment
credits — amounts that can be deducted from the tax
dependents — people who rely on someone for support
dividend income — money earned from stock holdings
exemptions — something that enables a worker to pay less tax
Internal Revenue Service (IRS) — the department of the federal
    government that collects federal income tax

ACTIVITIES

1. Have students investigate the origins of the federal income tax. They may be interested in finding out what powers of enforcement the IRS has and what, if any, restrictions Congress has placed on it.

2. Set up a role-playing situation, give necessary data, and have students fill out a 1040A form. If you'd like students to have more experience filling out income tax forms, you may wish to

bring in the 1040 form and have them itemize deductions, take tax credits, and so on.

3. Have a tax expert speak to the class and answer questions.

45. APPLICATION FOR CLASSIFIABLE FINGERPRINTS

This master is a copy of a fingerprint record used by various government agencies, including the armed forces, the Veterans Administration (for claims), the Justice Department (for citizenship applications), and law enforcement agencies. In order to actually use this master, you'll need a few inkpads.

VOCABULARY

alias — a name someone uses other than his or her real one
simultaneously — all at the same time

ACTIVITIES

1. Ask a law enforcement official to talk to the class about various aspects and uses of fingerprints to track down criminal suspects.

2. Have students find a fiction or nonfiction story (or write one of their own) about the use of fingerprints in a criminal case. Have students take turns reading the passages aloud to the class (or in small groups).

46, 47. APPLICATION FOR FOOD STAMPS

The Food Stamp Act was designed to help needy families or individuals receive an adequate diet by providing them with food coupons or stamps, which are used to buy food. This application is lengthy. Tell your students that the original form is several pages longer than the one they will fill out here. The original form asks for further details about all other income sources and about expenses such as medical and dependent care and shelter and utility costs. After the applicant fills out the form, he or she is interviewed by a social worker. The applicant needs to bring proof of income (such as wage stubs), utility bills, rent receipts, and bank statements to the interview. The social worker will then determine the applicant's eligibility based on these criteria.

VOCABULARY

audit — examination and review of accounts
facilitate — make easier
fraudulent — deceptive; based on trickery or deceit
mandatory — required

ACTIVITIES

1. We often read about fraud in the food stamp program. Ask students to research the program and find out the percentage of fraudulent claims. Have them weigh the program's advantages and disadvantages in a class discussion.

2. Ask a social worker to explain the program to your class.

48, 49. APPLICATION TO FILE PETITION FOR NATURALIZATION

This application is for those who want to become naturalized citizens of the United States. "Instructions to the Applicant" are reproduced in this teacher section on pages xxiii and xxiv. You may want to read the instructions aloud while students fill out the form. (Due to space limitations, a page of the original naturalization application form has been deleted; it deals with information on family, military service, and employment.) Since most students probably are unaware of what is required to become a naturalized United States citizen, these masters should lead to an interesting discussion. Master **49** asks for biographical information; students may use fictional information here, if they like.

VOCABULARY

advocate — to speak in favor of

affiliated — closely associated with

alien — a foreign-born resident of a country who has not been naturalized; aliens must register with the United States government

cited — named in a court summons

conscientious objection — refusal for moral or religious reasons to serve in the armed forces

deportation — removal of an alien from a country

extermination — getting rid of completely by killing off

hereditary — passed on from parent to child

illicit — unlawful

immigration — coming into a country to live permanently

incite — stir up; urge on

incompetent — not able to perform

indicted — charged with a crime

naturalization — being admitted as a citizen

noncombatant — someone who does not fight

oath of allegiance — a swearing of loyalty

polygamy — having more than one husband or wife at the same time

vigilante — a member of a volunteer group for stopping and punishing crime

ACTIVITIES

1. You may want to divide the class into several groups for this activity. National and state laws have been revoked, passed, and/or amended in response to an influx of refugees. Ask students to research immigration statistics (available in the reference section of most libraries) to find years when large swells of immigrants came to the United States. Then have them find immigration laws that correspond chronologically with that influx to see if they can discern a government policy toward a particular group of immigrants. (The most recent examples of this have been the influx of Vietnamese "boat people" in the mid-1970's and Cuban refugees in the early 1980's. However, the state of California responded to Chinese immigrants rather harshly as early as 1878.)

2. Ask students to note questions of particular interest to them as they fill out this petition (perhaps the oath of allegiance or the literacy test). Invite someone who is knowledgeable about naturalization laws to address their questions.

50. TELEGRAMS

Students can send telegrams from a local telegraph office, or they can telephone messages to the office. A telegraph operator types the message on a teleprinter, which punches holes in paper tape. The tape passes through on an automatic transmitter that sends messages to a message center. The center quickly routes the message from one area to another over the telegraph network. An operator flashes the message to its destination on a relaying machine. After the local office receives the telegram, it telephones the person to whom the message was sent. If this is impossible, the message is delivered. Messages are called "telegrams" or "wires" if they go over a land circuit. They are called "cables" if they go by cables under water.

Gifts and money can also be sent by telegraph. The rates are the same as those of telegrams plus a money order fee. In order to send or receive a money order, a person must know the correct "test question," which is given to the sender or receiver by the telegram agent. (The "test question" is referred to on the money order payment authorization form.) The correct response ensures that the money goes to the right person.

ACTIVITIES

1. Have students practice composing messages. This is good preparation for saying things concisely.

2. Have students research and report on the different kinds of transmitters used to send these messages.

3. Take a field trip to a telegraph office.

Application for Enlistment -
Armed Forces of the United States (Part IV)

37. CHARACTER AND SOCIAL ADJUSTMENT Read and consider the following instructions carefully BEFORE answering questions a through f

1. If your answer to every question is truthfully "NO", please indicate in the appropriate space.

2. If your answer to any questions in this item is "YES", or you have reservations about answering questions of this nature, you are not required to answer, or explain any of these questions in writing. Instead, you may request a personal interview in which you may provide the required information for each question orally.

3. If you choose the personal interview, the information you give may be investigated; however, any written record of the interview itself will not be retained more than six months after entry upon active duty, and it will not become a part of your permanent military personnel service record.

4. If you enlist, this information may be requested from you again at some future date and may become a part of your security investigative file at that time. This could occur as a result of your being considered for duties involving access to classified information or other types of duty requiring a personnel security investigation.

5. A "YES" answer will not necessarily disqualify you for enlistment. It will depend on the circumstances surrounding the situation involved.

INITIAL HERE IF YOU PREFER A PERSONAL INTERVIEW: _____

APPLICANT HAS BEEN INTERVIEWED AND IS ☐ ELIGIBLE FOR ENLISTMENT, ☐ INELIGIBLE FOR ENLISTMENT

DATE OF INTERVIEW	NAME, ORGANIZATION & TITLE	SIGNATURE OF INTERVIEWER

EXPLAIN "YES" ANSWERS IN ITEM 41:	NO	YES

a. HAVE YOU EVER TAKEN ANY NARCOTIC SUBSTANCE, SEDATIVE, STIMULANT, OR TRANQUILIZER DRUGS EXCEPT AS PRESCRIBED BY A LICENSED PHYSICIAN?

b. HAVE YOU EVER INTENTIONALLY SNIFFED GLUE, PAINT, HAIRSPRAY, OR OTHER CHEMICAL FUMES?

c. HAVE YOU EVER BEEN INVOLVED IN THE USE, PURCHASE, POSSESSION OR SALE OF MARIJUANA, LSD, OR ANY HARMFUL OR HABIT-FORMING DRUGS AND/OR CHEMICALS EXCEPT AS PRESCRIBED BY A LICENSED PHYSICIAN?

d. HAS YOUR USE OF ALCOHOLIC BEVERAGES (*SUCH AS LIQUOR, BEER, WINE*) EVER RESULTED IN THE LOSS OF A JOB, ARREST BY POLICE, or TREATMENT FOR ALCOHOLISM?

e HAVE YOU EVER BEEN A PATIENT (*WHETHER OR NOT FORMALLY COMMITTED*) IN ANY INSTITUTION PRIMARILY DEVOTED TO THE TREATMENT OF MENTAL, NERVOUS, EMOTIONAL, PSYCHOLOGICAL, OR PERSONALITY DISORDERS?

f. HAVE YOU EVER ENGAGED IN HOMOSEXUAL ACTIVITY (SEXUAL RELATIONS WITH ANOTHER PERSON OF THE SAME SEX)?

38. MARITAL STATUS AND DEPENDENCY | NO | YES

a. ARE YOU NOW, OR HAVE YOU EVER BEEN MARRIED?

b. IF YOU HAVE BEEN MARRIED, ARE YOU NOW LIVING WITH YOUR SPOUSE?

c. HAVE YOU EVER BEEN DIVORCED? (If yes, enter date, place and court which granted divorce or legal separation)

d. IS ANY COURT ORDER OR JUDGEMENT DIRECTING SUPPORT FOR CHILDREN OF ALIMONY IN EFFECT? (Enter date, place, and court which granted alimony decree, or support as the result of a paternity suit)

e. IS ANYONE OTHER THAN YOUR SPOUSE AND/OR CHILDREN SOLELY OR PARTIALLY DEPENDENT UPON YOU? (list name & address)

39. Do you now have, or within the past ten years, have you had knowing membership with the specific intent of furthering the aims of, or adherence to and active participation in any foreign or domestic organizations, association, movement, group, or combination of persons (hereinafter referred to as organizations) which unlawfully advocates or practices the commission of acts of force or violence to prevent others from exercising their rights under the Constitution or laws of the United States or of any State, or which seeks to overthrow the Government of the United States or any State or subdivision thereof by unlawful means?

If you answered "yes", give the names of the organizations and inclusive dates (month and year) of your membership; describe the nature of your activities as a member of the organization(s) in the "Remarks" section, Item 41. | NO | YES

40 INVOLVEMENT WITH POLICE OR JUDICIAL AUTHORITIES

YOUR ANSWERS TO THE FOLLOWING QUESTIONS WILL BE VERIFIED WITH THE FEDERAL BUREAU OF INVESTIGATION (FBI), AND OTHER AGENCIES, TO DETERMINE ANY PREVIOUS RECORDS OF ARREST OR CONVICTIONS OR JUVENILE COURT ADJUDICATIONS. IF YOU CONCEAL SUCH RECORDS AT THIS TIME, YOU MAY, UPON ENLISTMENT, BE SUBJECT TO DISCIPLINARY ACTION UNDER THE UNIFORM CODE OF MILITARY JUSTICE AND/OR DISCHARGE FROM THE MILITARY SERVICE WITH OTHER THAN AN HONORABLE DISCHARGE. | NO | YES

a Have you ever been arrested, charged, cited, or held by Federal, State, or other law enforcement or juvenile authorities regardless of whether the citation or charge was dropped or dismissed or you were found not guilty?

b. As a result of being arrested, charged, cited, or held by law enforcement or juvenile authorities, have you ever been convicted, fined by or forfeited bond to a Federal, State, or other judicial authority or adjudicated a youthful offender or juvenile delinquent (regardless of whether the record in your case has been "sealed" or otherwise stricken from the court record)?

c. Have you ever been detained, held in, or served time in, any jail or prison, or reform or industrial school or any juvenile facility or institution under the jurisdiction of any City, County, State, Federal or foreign country?

d. Have you ever been awarded, or are you now under suspended sentence, parole, or probation or awaiting any action on charges against you?

40. Continued | NO | YES

e. HAVE YOU BEEN RELEASED FROM PAROLE, PROBATION, JUVENILE SUPERVISION, OR GIVEN A SUSPENDED SENTENCE OR RELIEVED OF CHARGES PENDING ON CONDITION THAT YOU APPLY FOR OR ENLIST IN THE US ARMED FORCES?

f. ARE YOU NOW INVOLVED IN OR A PARTY TO OR CONNECTED WITH ANY COURT ACTION OR CIVIL SUIT? (EXPLAIN "YES" ANSWER IN ITEM 41)

g. EXPLAIN BELOW "YES" ANSWERS IN "a" THROUGH "e". BE CAREFUL TO INCLUDE *ALL* INCIDENTS WITH LAW ENFORCEMENT AUTHORITIES THAT YOU DISCUSSED WITH YOUR RECRUITER.

OFFENSE	DATE/PLACE	AGE	DISPOSITION	COURT

41. REMARKS

UNITED STATES DEPARTMENT OF JUSTICE
IMMIGRATION AND NATURALIZATION SERVICE

APPLICATION TO FILE PETITION FOR NATURALIZATION

INSTRUCTIONS TO THE APPLICANT

(Tear off this instruction sheet before filling out this form)

You must be at least 18 years old to file a petition for naturalization. Using ink or a typewriter, answer every question in the application form, whether you are male or female. If you need more space for an answer, write "Continued" in your answer, then finish your answer on a sheet of paper this size, giving the number of the question.

YOU WILL BE EXAMINED UNDER OATH ON THE ANSWERS IN THIS APPLICATION WHEN YOU APPEAR FOR YOUR NATURALIZATION EXAMINATION.

If you wish to be called for examination at the same time as a relative who is applying for naturalization is called, attach a separate sheet so stating, and show the name and the Alien Registration Number of that relative.

1. **YOU MUST SEND WITH THIS APPLICATION THE FOLLOWING ITEMS (1), (2), (3) AND (4):**

   (1) **Photographs of your Face:**

   a. Three identical unglazed copies, size 2 x 2 inches only.

   b. Taken within the last 30 days.

   c. Distance from top of head to point of chin to be 1¼ inches.

   d. On thin paper, with light background, showing front view without hat.

   e. In natural color or black and white, and not machine-made.

   f. Unsigned (but write Alien Registration Number lightly in pencil in center of reverse side).

   (2) **Fingerprint Chart**—Complete all personal data items such as name, address, date of birth, sex, etc. Write your Alien Registration Number in the space marked "Your No. OCA" or "Miscellaneous No. MNU". You must sign the chart IN THE PRESENCE OF THE PERSON taking your fingerprints and have that person sign his/her name, title and date in the spaces provided. Take the chart and these instructions to a police station, sheriff's office, ▮▮▮▮▮ ▮▮▮▮▮, or other reputable person or organization for fingerprinting. (You should contact the police or sheriff's office first since some of these offices do not take fingerprints for other government agencies.) DO NOT BEND, FOLD OR CREASE THE FINGERPRINT CHART.

   (3) **Biographic Information.**—Complete every item in the Biographic Information form furnished you with this application and sign your name on the line provided. If you have ever served in the Armed Forces of the United States, obtain and complete also an extra yellow sheet of the form, bearing the number G-325B.

   (4) **U.S. Military Service.**—If your application is based on your military service, obtain and complete Form N—426, "Request for Certification of Military or Naval Service."

2. **FEE.**—DO NOT SEND any fee with this application unless you are also applying for a certificate of citizenship for a child (see Instruction 6).

3. **ALIEN REGISTRATION RECEIPT CARD.**—DO NOT SEND your Alien Registration Receipt Card with this application.

4. **EXAMINATION ON GOVERNMENT AND LITERACY.**—Every person applying for naturalization must show that he or she has a knowledge and understanding of the history, principles, and form of government of the United States. THERE IS NO EXEMPTION FROM THIS REQUIREMENT, and you will therefore be examined on these subjects when you appear before the examiner with your witnesses.

   You will also be examined on your ability to read, write and speak English. If on the date of your examination you are more than 50 years of age and have been a lawful permanent resident of the United States for 20 or more years, you will be exempt from the English language requirements of the law. If you are exempt, you may take the examination in any language you wish.

5. **OATH OF ALLEGIANCE.**—You will be required to take the following oath of allegiance to the United States in order to become a citizen:

I hereby declare, on oath, that I absolutely and entirely renounce and abjure all allegiance and fidelity to any foreign prince, potentate, state or sovereignty, of whom or which I have heretofore been a subject or citizen; that I will support and defend the Constitution and laws of the United States of America against all enemies, foreign and domestic; that I will bear true faith and allegiance to the same; that I will bear arms on behalf of the United States when required by the law; that I will perform noncombatant service in the armed forces of the United States when required by the law; that I will perform work of national importance under civilian direction when required by the law; and that I take this obligation freely without any mental reservation or purpose of evasion; so help me God.

If you cannot promise to bear arms or perform noncombatant service because of religious training and belief, you may omit those promises when taking the oath.

"Religious training and belief" means a person's belief in a relation to a Supreme Being involving duties superior to those arising from any human relation, but does not include essentially political, sociological, or philosophical views or a merely personal moral code.

---

6. THIS BLOCK APPLIES ONLY TO APPLICANTS WHO HAVE FOREIGN-BORN CHILDREN WHO ARE UNDER 18 YEARS OF AGE.

Some or all of your *own* foreign-born children (Not Step-Children) who are not yet citizens may possibly become United States citizens automatically when you are naturalized. This will happen:

(1) If the child is a lawful permanent resident of the United States and still under 18 years of age when you are naturalized, and

(2) The child's other parent is already a citizen or becomes a citizen before or at the same time that you become naturalized. If, however, the child's other parent is deceased, or if you are divorced and have custody of the child, then it makes no difference that the child's other parent was or is an alien.

(3) If your child is illegitimate and you are the mother, only (1) above applies.

(4) If the child is adopted, and was adopted before its 16th birthday and is in your custody.

If you wish, you can apply for a Certificate of Citizenship for any of these children, which will show that they are United States citizens. If you do not want such a Certificate, write "DO NOT" in Question (36), page 3; if you do want such a Certificate, write "DO" in Question (36), page 3, and send the following with this application.

(1) **Fee.** Fifteen dollars ($15) for each child for whom a certificate is desired. DO NOT SEND CASH IN THE MAIL. ALL FEES MUST BE SUBMITTED IN THE EXACT AMOUNT. If you mail your application, attach a money order or check, payable to *Immigration and Naturalization Service*, (Exceptions: If you reside in the Virgin Islands, remittance must be payable to Commissioner of Finance, Virgin Islands; and if in Guam, to Treasurer, Guam). Personal checks are accepted subject to collectibility. An uncollectible check will render the application and any documents issued pursuant thereto invalid. A charge of $5.00 will be imposed if a check in payment of a fee is not honored by the bank on which it is drawn. The fee will be refunded if for any reason the child does not qualify for the certificate.

(2) **Personal Description Form.**—A completed Form N—604 for each child.

(3) **Documents.**—The documents applicable to your case listed in the blocks below. If you want any of the original documents returned to you, and if the law does not prohibit the making of copies, a photocopy of the document should be sent with the original document.

Any document in a foreign language must be accompanied by an English translation. The translation must contain a certification from the translator as to his competency as a translator and the accuracy of his translation.

(4) **Photographs.**—Follow Instruction No. one (1) and send three (3) photographs of each child. Write the child's Alien Registration Number on the back of the photographs, lightly in pencil.

DOCUMENTS REQUIRED WITH THIS APPLICATION

1. Child's birth certificate.
2. Your marriage certificate to child's other parent.
3. If you or the other parent were married before the marriage to each other, death certificate or divorce decree showing the termination of any previous marriage of each parent.
4. If the other parent became a citizen at birth, birth certificate of other parent.
5. If the child's other parent is deceased, or if you are divorced from the child's other parent, the death certificate or the divorce decree.
6. If the child is adopted, adoption decree.

SECONDARY EVIDENCE

If it is not possible to obtain any one of the required documents shown in the block above, consideration may be given to the following documents. In such case you must present a written explanation as to why the document listed in the block above is not being presented, together with a statement from the official custodian of the record showing that the document is not available.

1. *Baptismal certificate.*—A certificate under the seal of the church where the baptism occurred, showing date and place of child's birth, date of baptism, the names of the child's parents, and names of the godparents, if shown.
2. *School record.*—A letter from the school authorities having jurisdiction over the school attended (preferably the first school), showing date of admission to the school, child's date of birth or age at that time, place of birth, and the names and places of birth of parents, if shown in the school records.
3. If you or the other parent were married before the marriage to each other, death certificate or divorce decree showing the termination of any person(s) listed.
4. *Affidavits.*—Notarized affidavits of two persons who were living at the time, and who have personal knowledge of the event you are trying to prove—for example, the date and place of a birth, marriage, or death. The persons making the affidavits may be relatives and need not be citizens of the United States. Each affidavit should contain the following information regarding the person making the affidavit; His (Her) full name and address; date and place of birth; relationship to you, if any; full information concerning the event; and complete details concerning how he (she) acquired knowledge of the event.

DEPARTMENT OF HEALTH AND HUMAN SERVICES
SOCIAL SECURITY ADMINISTRATION

Form Approved
OMB No. 0960-0066

FORM SS-5 — APPLICATION FOR A SOCIAL SECURITY NUMBER CARD
(Original, Replacement or Correction)

MICROFILM REF. NO. (SSA USE ONLY)

Unless the requested information is provided, we may not be able to issue a Social Security Number (20 CFR, 103(b))

INSTRUCTIONS TO APPLICANT ▶ Before completing this form, please read the instructions on the opposite page. You can type or print, using pen with dark blue or black ink. Do not use pencil.

1

NAA	NAME TO BE SHOWN ON CARD	First	Middle	Last
NAB	FULL NAME AT BIRTH (IF OTHER THAN ABOVE)	First	Middle	Last
ONA	OTHER NAME(S) USED			

2

| STT | MAILING ADDRESS | (Street/Apt No , P O Box, Rural Route No.) | | |
| CTY STE ZIP | CITY | | STATE | ZIP CODE |

3 CSP — CITIZENSHIP (Check one only)

- ☐ a. U.S. citizen
- ☐ b. Legal alien allowed to work
- ☐ c. Legal alien not allowed to work
- ☐ d. Other (See instructions on Page 2)

4 SEX
- ☐ Male
- ☐ Female

5 SEX ETB — RACE/ETHNIC DESCRIPTION (Check one only) (Voluntary)
- ☐ a. Asian, Asian-American or Pacific Islander (Includes persons of Chinese, Filipino, Japanese, Korean, Samoan, etc., ancestry or descent)
- ☐ b. Hispanic (Includes persons of Chicano, Cuban, Mexican or Mexican-American, Puerto Rican, South or Central American, or other Spanish ancestry or descent)
- ☐ c. Negro or Black (not Hispanic)
- ☐ d. North American Indian or Alaskan Native
- ☐ e. White (not Hispanic)

6 DOB — DATE OF BIRTH | MONTH | DAY | YEAR **7** AGE PRESENT AGE **8** PLB PLACE OF BIRTH | CITY | STATE OR FOREIGN COUNTRY

9

| MNA | MOTHER'S NAME AT HER BIRTH | First | Middle | Last (her maiden name) |
| FNA | FATHER'S NAME | First | Middle | Last |

10

PNO a. Have you or someone on your behalf applied for a social security number before? ☐ No ☐ Don't Know ☐ Yes
If you checked "yes", complete items "b" through "c" below; otherwise go to item 11.

SSN PNS PNY b. Enter social security number

c. In what State did you apply? | What year?

NLC d. Enter the name shown on your most recent social security card

e. If the birth date you used was different from the date shown in item 6, enter it here. | MONTH | DAY | YEAR

11 DON — TODAY'S DATE ▶ | MONTH | DAY | YEAR

12 Telephone number where we can reach you during the day ▶ | HOME | OTHER

ASD — WARNING: Deliberately providing false information on this application is punishable by a fine of $1,000 or one year in jail, or both.

13 YOUR SIGNATURE

14 YOUR RELATIONSHIP TO PERSON IN ITEM 1
- ☐ Self
- ☐ Other (Specify) _____

WITNESS (Needed only if signed by mark "X") | WITNESS (Needed only if signed by mark "X")

DO NOT WRITE BELOW THIS LINE (FOR SSA USE ONLY) | DTC | SSA RECEIPT DATE _____

☐ SUPPORTING DOCUMENT- EXPEDITE CASE
☐ DUP ISSUED | SSN ASSIGNED OR VERIFIED | SSN

NPN

| DOC | NTC | CAN | BIC | SIGNATURE AND TITLE OF EMPLOYEE(S) REVIEWING EVIDENCE AND/OR CONDUCTING INTERVIEW. |

TYPE(S) OF EVIDENCE SUBMITTED

☐ MANDATORY IN PERSON INTERVIEW CONDUCTED | DATE

DATE

IDN ITV DCL

Form **SS-5** (2-81)

PROMISE OF VACATION EMPLOYMENT

PROMISE OF VACATION EMPLOYMENT (This is NOT an employment certificate.)
(This record must be kept for inspection in the files of the issuing officer.)

Commonwealth of Pennsylvania
DEPARTMENT OF EDUCATION

A. This section to be completed by the issuing officer.

Date of Application _____

Name of Minor _____ Highest Grade Completed _____

Vacation Employment Certificate No. _____

Evidence of age accepted and filed. Evidence shall be required in the order designated. Cross out all but the one accepted.

(a) Birth Certificate.
(b) Baptismal Certificate.
(c) Passport.
(d) Other documentary evidence (other than a school record)
(e) Affidavit of parent or guardian accompanied by physician's statement of opinion as to the age of minor.

Date Issued _____
Date Returned _____

Date of Birth of Minor		
Month	Day	Year

Signature of Issuing Officer _____

Name of School District _____

B. This section to be completed by the prospective employer.

The undersigned expects to employ _____ as _____ Kind of Work (Specify machine, if any) _____

according to the following schedule of hours:

	Sunday		Monday		Tuesday		Wednesday		Thursday		Friday		Saturday		Total Hours Per Week
	From	To	From	To	From	To	From	To	From	To	From	To	From	To	
During the School year { A.M. / P.M.															
During Summer Vacation { A.M. / P.M.															

Name of Firm _____

Telephone Number _____

Kind of Industry _____

Signature of Owner, Superintendent or Manager _____

Address _____

C. This section to be completed by the parent or guardian.

I, the parent or guardian of the above minor, do hereby agree to the issuance of an employment certificate for his employment under the above stipulations.

Signature of Parent or Guardian _____

Address _____

Application for the employment certificate must be made in person by the parent, guardian or legal custodian, except for minors who show official proof of graduation from accredited senior high schools.

DEBE-168 (8-72)

DIRECTIONS TO MINOR

1. Secure evidence of age as indicated in section A.

2. Take the blank to the employer to complete section B.

3. Take the blank to the authorized physician who will complete the Record of Physical Examination.

4. Take the completed blank to the school district official who issues certificates.

DIRECTIONS TO EMPLOYER

1. Fill out blanks in section B and give the form to the minor. The Vacation Employment Certificate will be mailed to you.

2. Every employer must have a Vacation Employment Certificate before he permits minors 14 through 17 years of age to work at times that will not interfere with regular school attendance; also required for male minors ages 12 and 13 employed as caddies.

   Exception: Minors 17 years of age who have graduated from an accredited senior high school, or who are no longer on the active school roll, are not required to have Vacation Employment Certificate.

3. **Maximum Legal Hours:**

   Minors under 18 years of age may not be employed more than eight hours a day, 44 hours a week, six days a week; nor more than five hours continuously without an interval of 30 minutes for lunch.

   Other Hourly Limitations:
   Students ages 16 and 17 years may not be employed for more than 28 hours per school week during the school term.
   (over)

EMPLOYMENT SECURITY COMMISSION OF NORTH CAROLINA
UNEMPLOYMENT INSURANCE DIVISION
INITIAL CLAIM FOR BENEFITS AND NOTICE TO LAST EMPLOYER

( ) New   ( ) Additional

( ) UI   ( ) UCFE   ( ) UCX   ( ) ____

Claimant SS #_____

Name_____

Street
Address_____

City,
State & Zip_____

Telephone #_____

LAST EMPLOYER

Name_____

Street
Address_____

City,
State & Zip_____

SEPARATION INFORMATION FURNISHED BY CLAIMANT

Last Date Worked_____ . I no longer

have this job because:_____

_____

_____

Eff. Date	( ) ( ) M (1) F (2)
Yr. Born	E/R
L.O.	Co. of Res.
SIC Code (2)	Occupational Code (4)
Date of Filing	

A. Did you receive or will you receive any payment from your employer other than for work done during your last pay period? - For example, vacation pay or severance pay. - (If "yes", explain) ( ) No ( ) Yes

B. Did you work under another name or Social Security No. during the past 2 years? If "yes", enter the name and/or number _____ ( ) No ( ) Yes

C. Have you worked for the Federal Government, served in the Armed Forces, or worked as a Professional Athlete or as an Alien during the past 2 years? ( ) No ( ) Yes

D. Have you applied for or are you attending school or vocational training? ( ) No ( ) Yes

E. Are you seeking or receiving help, assistance, any kind of benefits, training, or employment under any government program? ( ) No ( ) Yes

F. Have you refused any work since you became unemployed? ( ) No ( ) Yes

G. Have you been customarily self-employed? ( ) No ( ) Yes

If any item C-G checked "yes", explain_____

H Have you applied for, will receive, or are you receiving any type of retirement pension? If "yes", and now receiving, have Form NCUI 563-R prepared by the Interviewer ( ) No ( ) Yes

I certify that my answers given above are correct; that I am unemployed and I will accept suitable work. I hereby register for work and claim benefits under the Employment Security Law of North Carolina and/or Federal Law (5 USC CH85). I have been informed of the method to follow to continue my claim for benefits. I understand there are penalties for making false statements in order to receive benefits.

_____
Claimant's Signature

I certify that this claimant has met the registration for work requirements, and that I have explained the eligibility requirements and the fraud penalties of the Employment Security Law.

_____
Interviewer

CENTRAL OFFICE COPY

TS-180 (7-70)

COMMONWEALTH OF PENNSYLVANIA
DEPARTMENT OF TRANSPORTATION
BUREAU OF TRAFFIC SAFETY
HARRISBURG 17123

**APPLICATION FOR LEARNER'S
PERMIT, EXAMINATION, JUNIOR
OPERATOR'S LICENSE , AND
OPERATOR'S LICENSE**

▼

Phys. Exam. On File And Approved

Being duly sworn makes application for Learner's Permit Examination, and Operator's License and states that (she) (he) is the applicant described below and that the answers made herein are true and correct.
PENALTY - Failure to furnish correct information will result in a one (1) year suspension of operating privileges.
FEE for Learner's Permit, Examination, and Operator's License is four dollars ($4.00).
DO NOT SEND CASH - - - Payment may be made by check or money order drawn to the order of the Pennsylvania Department of Transportation. Forward it together with this application to the Bureau of Motor Vehicles , Commonwealth of Pennsylvania, Harrisburg, Pa. 17122.
Checks are received subject to final payment and at the risk of the payer.
When filling out address, if a street and number are assigned to your residence, it must be shown.

FOR MAILING PURPOSES AND DEPARTMENTAL USE ONLY

S A M P L E

RESTRICTIONS =

= PHYSICAL EXAM DATE

(SEE REVERSE SIDE)

PRINT OR TYPEWRITE ALL INFORMATION IN FULL

1. LAST NAME	FIRST NAME (No Nicknames)	MIDDLE NAME

2. DATE OF BIRTH			3. AGE	4. SEX	5. WEIGHT (lbs.)	6. HEIGHT		COLOR	
Month	Day	Year				Ft.	Inches	7. Eyes	8. Hair

9. STREET ADDRESS (See instructions above)

CITY	COUNTY	STATE	ZIP CODE

(right margin, vertical) LEARNER'S PERMIT NUMBER

10. Have you heretofore been licensed or privileged to operate a motor vehicle in this or any other state? _____ If so, give year
Yes   No
and state in which you last held such license or privilege. _____
(Year)   (State)
11. Has your right to apply for such license or your privileges to operate in this or any other state ever been suspended or revoked? _____
Yes   No
If so, give place, date and reason
12. Has your license, right to apply or operating privilege been restored? _____ .
Yes   No
13. Have you ever been convicted of any violation in the operation of a motor vehicle, or any crime in the commission of which a motor vehicle was used? _____ If so, give particulars.
Yes   No
14. Are you able to understand warning or direction signals in English? _____ .
Yes   No
15. Have you any mental or physical incapacity or infirmity? _____ If so, give particulars _____
Yes   No
16. Are there any UNPAID judgements resulting from a motor vehicle accident recorded against you? _____ If "YES" give amounts
Yes   No

NOTE: Your license, when issued, will expire on the last day of your birth month, but will not exceed one year.

SEAL

Subscribed and sworn to before me this _____
day of _____ 19 _____

(Signature in Ink of Person Administering Oath)   Municipality

(Address in Ink of Person Administering Oath)   County
My Commission Expires _____ 19 _____

Applicant's Signature in Ink, or Mark properly witnessed - Signature must be the same as name furnished in Block #1

(Print name in ink exactly as it appears above in Signature)

AFFIDAVIT OF CONSENT OF PARENT OR PERSON IN LOCO PARENTIS

I hereby certify that I am the _____ of the applicant named herein, who is less than eighteen (18) years of age and more than sixteen (16)
(Parent or Person in Loco Parentis)   years of age, and that this application is made with my full consent.
Subscribed and sworn to before me this _____
day of _____ 19 _____

SEAL

(Signature in Ink of Person Administering Oath)   Municipality

(Address in Ink of Person Administering Oath)   County
My Commission Expires _____ 19 _____

(Signature of Parent or Person in Loco Parentis)

MAIL APPLICATION TO THE BUREAU OF MOTOR VEHICLES, COMMONWEALTH OF PENNSYLVANIA, HARRISBURG, PA. 17122

NOTIFICATION OF CHANGE OF ADDRESS
ON EITHER REGISTRATION OR OPERATOR RECORDS, OR BOTH

PART I.   REGISTRATION
INFORMATION REQUESTED BELOW CAN BE OBTAINED FROM YOUR REGISTRATION CARD.

NAME_____

PRINT NAME EXACTLY AS IT APPEARS ON REGISTRATION CARD.

OLD ADDRESS		NEW ADDRESS	
Street and Number		Street and Number	
Post Office		Post Office	
State	Zip Code	State	Zip Code

LICENSE NUMBER	YEAR OF ISSUE	MAKE OF CAR	MANUFACTURER'S NUMBER	CERTIFICATE OF TITLE NUMBER
	19			
	19			
	19			

- -

Part II   Operator (for one operator only)

PRINT INFORMATION EXACTLY AS IT APPEARS ON OPERATOR'S CARD

Name_____ _____ _____ _____
           Last   First   MI   (Jr. etc.)

Birth Date _____ _____ _____ Sex [   ] [   ] (Check one)
              Mo.   Day.   Yr.   M   F

OLD ADDRESS			NEW ADDRESS		
Street and Number			Street and Number		
Post Office (City)			Post Office (City)		
County	State	Zip Code	County	State	Zip Code

Operator Number_____

Signature_____
            (Applicant's signature in ink)

APPLICATION
for
INTERNATIONAL DRIVING PERMIT
or
INTER-AMERICAN DRIVING PERMIT

FEE FOR EACH PERMIT $5.00

Issuance of Permit is restricted to persons EIGHTEEN YEARS or over who hold a valid U.S.A. or Territorial License. PERMIT VALID FOR ONE YEAR. Not renewable.

CHECK DESIRED PERMIT

☐ International Driving Permit
(Fee $5.00 and 2 signed photos)

☐ Inter-American Driving Permit*** (See reverse side)
(Fee $5.00 and 2 signed photos)

MANDATORY REQUIREMENTS

(1) Attach 2 recent signed photos (2½"x2½") (2) Enclose permit fee of $5.00. (NO CASH).

NOTE: IT IS IMPORTANT THAT YOUR U.S.A. OR TERRITORIAL LICENSE BE CARRIED WITH THE PERMIT AT ALL TIMES. The International or Inter-American Driving Permit is not valid for driving in the United States.

Mr. Mrs. Miss Ms. (Circle One)   PRINT NAME IN FULL. No Initials

FIRST	MIDDLE	LAST
PHONE	HOME STREET ADDRESS	
CITY	STATE	ZIP CODE
U.S. DRIVER'S LICENSE NO.	STATE OF ISSUE	EXPIRATION DATE
BIRTHPLACE: CITY	STATE OR COUNTRY	BIRTH DATE (MO. DAY YEAR)
DATE PERMIT TO BE EFFECTIVE	DEPARTURE DATE FROM U.S.	
FOREIGN ADDRESS (If known)		

PLEASE CHECK THE APPROPRIATE BOX BELOW TO INDICATE THE TYPE OF VEHICLE FOR WHICH YOU NOW HOLD A VALID U.S.A. OR TERRITORIAL DRIVER'S LICENSE, AND FOR WHICH YOU DESIRE THIS PERMIT:

☐ MOTORCYCLE ☐ PASSENGER CAR ☐ VEHICLE OVER 7,700 LBS. ☐ VEHICLE OVER 8 SEATS ☐ VEHICLE WITH HEAVY TRAILER

I CERTIFY THAT THE ABOVE INFORMATION IS TRUE AND CORRECT, AND THAT THE LICENSE INDICATED HAS NOT BEEN SUSPENDED NOR REVOKED.
I FURTHER CERTIFY THAT I UNDERSTAND THAT A VALID STATE DRIVER'S LICENSE MUST ACCOMPANY THIS PERMIT, AND THAT THIS PERMIT IS VALID ONLY AS LONG AS THE STATE LICENSE IS VALID, BUT NOT TO EXCEED ONE YEAR FROM THE DATE THE PERMIT IS ISSUED.

SIGNATURE (signature mandatory for issuance of Permit)	DATE

THIS IS YOUR MAILING LABEL
Please print to ensure prompt delivery

MAIL ENTIRE APPLICATION TO:

NAME		
STREET		
CITY	STATE	ZIP CODE
COUNTRY		

NAME_____ **APPLICATION FOR**   7
Commonwealth of Pennsylvania   **CERTIFICATE OF TITLE**
Department of Transportation
Bureau of Motor Vehicles   **NOTE: M/S/O OR OUT-OF-STATE TITLE MUST BE ATTACHED**
Harrisburg, PA 17122

A | **GIVE ALL APPLICABLE INFORMATION REQUESTED**

CHECK (✓) PROPER BLOCK | New ☐ | Dealer ☐ | Out-of-State ☐ | Reconstructed ☐ | Specially Constructed ☐ | Transfer by operation of Law ☐

VEHICLE DESCRIPTION

Make of Vehicle	Body Style	Model Name	Model Year	Odometer Reading	Fuel

Vehicle Identification Number	**VERIFICATION OF VEHICLE IDENTIFICATION**

I hereby certify a legible tracing cannot be made and that I have personally inspected the number on the vehicle herein described and find the number to be

ATTACH TRACING OR PHOTOGRAPH HERE

1. Attach legible tracing or photograph of Vehicle Identification Number Plate.
2. If VIN Plate does not show GVWR attach photograph of Certification Label.
3. If no VIN Plate, Penna. Special Number Plate must be applied for on Form MV-41.
4. If legible tracing or photograph cannot be obtained, verification must be completed by Police or Inspection Mechanic.

Vehicle Identification Number

GVWR (If Applicable)

Police Dept. or Inspection Mechanic

Signature of Verifier | Inspection Mechanic No.

B | **VEHICLE TYPE** | **COMPLETE APPLICABLE SECTION FOR VEHICLE TYPE** | Dept. Use Only

Passenger
Seating Capacity | Used in Carpool ☐ Yes ☐ No

Motorcycle Motor Driven Cycle Motorized Pedalcycle
Cylinder Capacity | Maximum Design Speed | Operable Pedals ☐ YES ☐ NO | DEPT. USE ONLY
Brake Horsepower | Automatic Transmission ☐ YES ☐ NO

Truck Truck Tractor
No. of Axles | Requested Gross Wt. | Requested Gross Comb. Wt. (If applicable) | Max. Gross Wt. Rating
Width of Vehicle Excluding Tires | Width of Vehicle Including Tires | Rated Net Brake Horsepower | Tare (Empty) Wt.

USE FOR ADDITIONAL AXLE OR RECONSTRUCTED/SPECIALLY CONSTRUCTED VEHICLE

AXLES	FRONT	2nd	3rd	4th	5th
Wheels: Single or Dual					
Axle Capacity					

Motor Home
Chassis Name | Body Make | Gross Vehicle Wt.

Trailer Semi Trailer
Max. Gross Wt Rating | Requested Gross Wt. (Including Load) | No. of Axles | Dimensions: Length Width Height | Tare (Empty) Wt.

APPLICATION FOR SPECIAL NUMBER PLATE | Principal Parts Used:

I (We) make application for special vehicle Identification Plate for reason listed below:
☐ Lost ☐ Defaced ☐ Destroyed ☐ Other _____
☐ Specially constructed ☐ Reconstructed

If specially constructed or reconstructed list how constructed, attach three (3) photographs. If additional space is required attach separate sheets.

Bus
☐ School Bus Free ☐ Bus ☐ Mass Transportation ☐ Free | CHECK ONE IF APPLICABLE ☐ $10.00 Processing Fee ☐ Other | Check One If Applica. ☐ Pud ☐ Icc | Gross Wt. | Seating Capacity
☐ Yes ☐ No

Taxi
Seating Capacity | Gross Weight

Implement of Husbandry or Special Mobile Equipment
Gross Wt. | No. of Axles | Kind of Tires | Width of Vehicle Excluding Tires | Width of Vehicle Including Tires
Maximum Design Speed _____ Where is Vehicle Primarily Used _____
Describe Use of Vehicle _____

3 PHOTOS REQUIRED: SIDE, FRONT AND REAR VIEWS

C | **FROM WHOM ACQUIRED** | DATE ACQUIRED | **DEPT. USE ONLY**

NAME | ☐ M/S/O ATTACHED | ☐ OTHER

STREET ADDRESS | MUNICIPALITY | STATE | ☐ TITLE ATTACHED _____ STATE

D | CERTIFICATE OF TITLE APPLICATION — TITLE FEE $5.00 (Plus $5.00 Encumbrance Fee If Applicable)

I (WE) make application for Certificate of Title and certify that;(1)All information is true and correct; (2) The Vehicle conforms to equipment requirements of Part IV of the Vehicle Code and Department regulations; and (3) My (Our) Pennsylvania Registration is not suspended.

Applicant(s) Name

Street Address

Municipality | **State** | **Zip**

Signature of Individual or Authorized Person

X

Signature of Co-owner or Printed Name of Firm

X

Applicant(s) Telephone No. | **DIN (If Applicable)**

IS VEHICLE SUBJECT TO LIEN? ☐YES ☐NO

1st LIENHOLDER

Date of Lien | Amount of Lien

Name of Lienholder

Street Address

Municipality | State | Zip

SUBSCRIBED AND SWORN TO BEFORE ME

SEAL

Day | Month | Year

Signature of Person Administering Oath

Municipality | **County**

Commission Expiration

2nd LIENHOLDER

Date of Lien | Amount of Lien

Name of Lienholder

Street Address

Municipality | State | Zip

E | ASSIGNMENT OF TITLE

I (WE)warrant this Certificate of Title and Transfer Ownership of the vehicle described herein to the named purchaser, and further state that the vehicle is subject to no liens except as listed in Section D.

Signature of Seller or Authorized Person

X

Signature of Co-owner or Printed Name of Firm

X

PURCHASER'S NAME

STREET ADDRESS

MUNICIPALITY | **STATE** | **ZIP**

ODOMETER READING _____

☐ Acutal Mileage differs from the odometer reading for reasons other than calibration error and actual mileage is unknown.

WARNING: An inaccurate statement may make you liable for damages to your transferee, pursuant to 409(a) of the Motor Vehicle Information and Cost Savings Act of 1972.

IS VEHICLE SUBJECT TO LIEN ☐YES ☐NO

1st LIENHOLDER

Date of Lien | Amount of Lien

Name of Lienholder

Street Address

Municipality | State | Zip

2nd LIENHOLDER

Date of Lien | Amount of Lien

Name of Lienholder

Street Address

Municipality | State | Zip

F | APPLICATION FOR (Check Applicable Block)

☐ New registration plate

Metal Temp. Plate No.

☐ Transfer of Registration Plate No.

☐ Substitution and transfer of Registration Plate

REASON: ☐ Lost ☐ Stolen ☐ Defaced ☐ Never Received

*Current registration card for plate being transferred must be attached. If card is not attached, an additional fee of $3.00 is required.

DEPT. USE ONLY

☐ Number of Duplicate Registration Cards. ($1.00 additional fee for each duplicate card requested.)

Complete the following Insurance information or attach copy of binder.

Insurance Company Name

Policy No. | **Ins. Code #**

G | APPLICATION FOR CHANGE OF NAME

In connection with Transfer of Registration Plate.

Print Former or Incorrect Name

Reason for Change: ☐Divorce ☐ Marriage ☐ Court Order
☐Other _____

Print Correct Name

H | VERIFICATION OF RELATIONSHIP IN CONNECTION WITH TRANSFER OF PLATE. Plate may be transferred between spouses or between parent(s) [including step-parent(s) or parent(s)-in-law] and their child(ren) [including step-child(ren) or child(ren)-in-law] or to or from a vehicle leased by an individual under Section 1314(A) of the Vehicle Code.

Signature of Transferor(s)

X

Signature of Transferee(s)

X

Relationship

Relationship

I | AFFIDAVIT OF APPLICANT

SUBSCRIBED AND SWORN BEFORE ME

SEAL

Day | Month | Year

Signature of Person Administering Oath

Municipality | **County**

Commission Expiration

I (WE) make application for Certificate of Title and certify that (1) all information is true and correct; (2) The vehicle conforms to equipment requirements of Part IV of the Vehicle Code and Department regulations; and (3) My (Our) Pennsylvania Registration is not suspended.

Signature of Individual or Authorized Person

Signature of Co-owner or Printed Name of Firm

Applicant's Telephone No. | **Dealer's DIN (if applicable)**

10. SOCIAL SECURITY NO. (optional)

11. YOUR HIGH SCHOOL CODE

Enter the school code number from the College Board poster in your school and blacken the corresponding ovals. By entering your school code, you are authorizing that your high school be sent a copy of your report.

12. HOME PHONE NUMBER

AREA CODE

13. PRESENT GRADE LEVEL

If not in school or if your grade is not shown, blacken the oval beside "other."

- 9th grade
- 10th grade
- 11th grade
- 12th grade
- 1st year college
- 2nd year college
- other

14. REPORTS TO COLLEGES AND SCHOLARSHIP PROGRAMS

Enter the code numbers from the gray-bordered list in the *Student Bulletin* and blacken the corresponding ovals. Reports will be sent only to those recipients whose codes are entered here.

Three reports are prepaid with your test fee if they are requested on this form. Additional reports are $4.00 each.

Prepaid Reports

Additional Reports

15. THE COLLEGE HANDBOOK

Do you wish to order the 1982-83 edition of *The College Handbook* or *Index of Majors* or both at the reduced prices shown below?

- Yes, *The College Handbook* at $10.95 (A saving of $2.00)
- Yes, *Index of Majors* at $8.95 (A saving of $2.00)
- Yes, both books at $17.95
- No, I do not wish to order.

16. STUDENT DESCRIPTIVE QUESTIONNAIRE

Responses A, B, or C are ONLY for candidates who have previously submitted descriptive information.

Use this area to answer the Student Descriptive Questionnaire in the *Student Bulletin.*

25. Month Year
Jan / Feb / Mar / Apr / May / June / July / Aug / Sept / Oct / Nov / Dec

26. Month Year
Jan / Feb / Mar / Apr / May / June / July / Aug / Sept / Oct / Nov / Dec

33. CODE

17. FEES AND REMITTANCE

Scholastic Aptitude Test	$10.50
1, 2, or 3 Achievement Tests taken on one test date	$16.75
Overseas processing fee	$ 5.00
Late registration fee	$ 8.00
Standby (walk-in) registration fee	$20.00
Additional reports (See item 14.)	at $4.00 each
The College Handbook	$10.95
The Index of Majors	$ 8.95
Both books (See item 15.)	$17.95

Enter total here and in item 9. (Blacken the corresponding ovals.) → $

Make checks payable to:
ADMISSIONS TESTING PROGRAM

- Do not send cash or stamps.
- Do not staple your check or money order to this form.

DO NOT WRITE IN THIS AREA. ETS USE ONLY

18. SIGNATURE

I agree to the conditions in the *Student Bulletin* concerning the administration of the tests and the reporting of scores and descriptive information.

(Sign) _____

19. YOUR MAILING ADDRESS Print complete address below.

Number and Street

Apartment (if any)

City

State

Zip Code

9

COLLEGE ADMISSION APPLICATION

SECTION I

Joseph A. Coldren
Application for Admission
Director of Admissions **LOCK HAVEN STATE COLLEGE, Lock Haven, Pa. 17745**

Please read Instruction Sheet before completing application.

1. Social Security Number |_|_|_| |_|_| |_|_|_|_| Sex |_| (M or F)

2.   Last Name   1st & Middle Name (abbreviate middle if necessary)
|_|_|_|_|_|_|_|_|_|_|_|_|_|_|_|_|_| |_|_|_|_|_|_|_|_|_|_|_|_|_|_|_|_|_|_|_|_|

3.   Legal Street Address   Area Code   Home Phone No.   Check if unlisted
|_|_|_|_|_|_|_|_|_|_|_|_|_|_|_|_|_| |_|_|_| |_|_|_| |_|_|_|_| |_|

4.   Legal City   State   Zip Code   County
|_|_|_|_|_|_|_|_|_|_|_|_|_|_|_|_| |_|_|_| |_|_|_|_|_| |_|_|_|_|_|_|_|

5.   Parent/Guardian/Spouse (last name)   1st & Middle Name (abbreviate middle)   Mr./Mrs./Miss
|_|_|_|_|_|_|_|_|_|_|_|_|_|_|_|_| |_|_|_|_|_|_|_|_|_|_|_|_| |_|_|_|_|_|

6. Relationship of line 5 (enter P=parent, G=guardian, S=spouse) |_|

7. Father's occupation_____ Mother's occupation _____

8. Total number of brothers and sisters supported by parents _____

9. Your date of birth Mo |_|_| Day |_|_| Yr |_|_| When do you plan to enter Lock Haven? Mo |_|_| Yr |_|_|

10. Have you previously applied to Lock Haven? Yes |_| No |_| When?_____(date)

11. Marital Status (enter S=single, M=married, D=divorced, W=widowed) |_|

12. Do you plan to be a (check one) Full-time Student |_| Part-time Student |_|

13. Curriculum to which you seek admission (refer to enclosed code sheet)
curriculum:_____ code number: |_|_|_|

14. What are your career objectives?_____

15. Are you a (check one) New Student |_| Transfer Student |_|

16. Do you plan to (check one) Live on Campus |_| Live in Town |_| Commute from Home |_|

17. Are you an applicant for financial aid? Yes |_| No |_| If "yes" have you filed a PCS?_____

18. Do you have a scholarship or loan?_____ If "yes" give name and provisions _____

19. Are you a veteran?_____ Dates of Service: from Mo |_|_| Yr |_|_| to Mo |_|_| Yr |_|_|

20. By request of the Pa. Human Relations Commission, please give the following:
National Origin_____ Religious Preference _____
Race_____ Check here |_| if you do not wish to disclose this information.

21. Are you a citizen of the United States?_____ If not, what is your visa status?_____
_____ Are you a legal resident of Pa.?_____

22. Name of High School_____ Phone Number |_|_|_|_| |_|_|_|_| |_|_|_|_|
Street Address_____ City & State_____ Zip_____

23. High School College Board Code number (see guidance counselor) |_|_|_|_|_|_|_|

24. Date of Graduation Mo |_|_| Yr |_|_|

NAME_____ DATE _____

COLLEGE ADMISSION APPLICATION

25. Have you attended another college?_____ If "yes" list name(s) of institution(s)

Name	Location	Dates Attended	College Board Code No.	Full Time	Part Time
_____	_____	_____	⊔⊔⊔⊔	⊔	⊔
_____	_____	_____	⊔⊔⊔⊔	⊔	⊔
_____	_____	_____	⊔⊔⊔⊔	⊔	⊔

26. Reason(s) for wishing to transfer?_____

_____

27. Date you took your Junior Year SAT?   Mo ⊔⊔   Yr ⊔⊔

28. Date you took (or plan to take) your Senior Year SAT?   Mo ⊔⊔   Yr ⊔⊔

29. Date you took (or plan to take) your ACT?   Mo ⊔⊔   Yr ⊔⊔

30. Do you have any health condition of which this college should be aware if you are admitted?

    Yes ⊔   No ⊔   If "yes" please explain _____

_____

31. Check the appropriate blocks for high school activities in which you participated and for activities in which you expect to participate while in college.

	H.S.		College			H.S.		College
Debating	⊔	(10)	⊔	Lacrosse	⊔	(23)	⊔
Dramatics	⊔	(11)	⊔	Wrestling	⊔	(24)	⊔
Student Gov't	⊔	(12)	⊔	Golf	⊔	(25)	⊔
Band	⊔	(13)	⊔	Swimming	⊔	(26)	⊔
Orchestra	⊔	(14)	⊔	Cross Country	⊔	(27)	⊔
Majorette	⊔	(15)	⊔	Tennis	⊔	(28)	⊔
Yearbook	⊔	(16)	⊔	Softball	⊔	(29)	⊔
School Paper	⊔	(17)	⊔	Gymnastics	⊔	(30)	⊔
Field Hockey	⊔	(18)	⊔	Cheerleader	⊔	(31)	⊔
Baseball	⊔	(19)	⊔	Class Officer	⊔	(32)	⊔
Football	⊔	(20)	⊔	Soccer	⊔	(33)	⊔
Track	⊔	(21)	⊔	Field Archery	⊔	(34)	⊔
Basketball	⊔	(22)	⊔	Chorus	⊔	(35)	⊔
			Other: _____				⊔

32. List any honors received in the above activities _____

I certify that the information provided is correct. I further certify that, if accepted, I will abide by the rules and regulations set forth by Lock Haven State College.

_____   _____
Signature of Applicant   Date

To the Principal, Headmaster, or Guidance Counselor:

The applicant should have submitted to you the *complete* application, consisting of Section I (personal information), Section II (Secondary School form or your equivalent form), the Applicant Index Card and a $10 check.

Please submit all sections of the application to the Office of Admissions, Sullivan Hall, Lock Haven State College, Lock Haven, Pennsylvania 17745. (Section III, the Medical Examination Report, is to be submitted by the examining physician.)

C

NO. _____

_____ 19 ___

TO _____

FOR _____

	DOLLARS	CENTS
BAL. BRO'T FOR'D		
AMT DEPOSITED		
" "		
" "		
TOTAL		
AMT THIS CHECK		
BAL. CAR'D FOR'D		

central counties bank

pennsylvania

NO. _____

19 ___   60-559 / 313

PAY TO THE ORDER OF _____

$ _____

_____ DOLLARS

sample

⑆0313⑈0559⑆ 01⑈01709⑈

SMITH PRINTING CO WILLIAMSPORT PA

A

(1) SIGNATURE	CHECKING—JOINT SURVIVORSHIP ACCOUNT
(2) SIGNATURE	
	No. _____
NAMES	

CENTRAL COUNTIES BANK, STATE COLLEGE, PA.

ADDRESS _____

DATE OPENED	INITIAL DEPOSIT	ACCOUNT OPENED BY
	$	

You are authorized to recognize any of the signatures subscribed above in the payment of funds or the transaction of any business for this account. It is agreed that all transactions between you and the undersigned shall be governed by the contract printed on the reverse side of this card.

The undersigned, joint depositors, hereby agree each with the other and with you that all sums now on deposit or heretofore or hereafter deposited by either or both of said joint depositors with you to their credit as such joint depositors with all accumulations thereon, are and shall be owned by them jointly, with right of survivorship, and be subject to the check or receipt of either of them or the survivor of them and payment to or on the check of either or the survivor shall be valid and discharge you from liability.

Each of the undersigned appoints the other attorney, with power to deposit in said joint account moneys of the other and for that purpose to endorse any check, draft, note or other instrument payable to the order of the other or both said joint depositors.

Payment to or on check of the survivor shall be subject to the laws relating to inheritance and succession taxes and all rules and regulations made pursuant thereto.

Your rights or authority under this agreement shall not be changed or terminated by us or either of us except by written notice to you which shall not affect transactions theretofore made.

B

SAVINGS—INDIVIDUAL

NAME _____

ADDRESS _____   No. _____

CENTRAL COUNTIES BANK, STATE COLLEGE, PA.

You are authorized to recognize the signature subscribed below in the payment of funds or the transaction of any business for this account. It is agreed that all transactions between the bank and the undersigned shall be governed by the contracts printed on the reverse side of this card. The undersigned has read the rules and regulations of the Savings Department now in effect and agrees thereto and to all changes therein or additions thereto which shall have been posted in the main lobby of the bank for five consecutive business days.

AUTHORIZED SIGNATURE (S) OF

Owner _____

Deputy _____

Deputy _____

DATE OPENED _____   INITIAL DEPOSIT $ _____

SIGNATURE AUTHORITY DATED _____   ACCOUNT OPENED BY _____

D

DEPOSITED IN

CENTRAL COUNTIES BANK

STATE COLLEGE, PA.

ACCOUNT NUMBER

DATE _____

PLEASE WRITE YOUR NAME _____

ALL DEPOSITS
SUBJECT TO VERIFICATION AND COLLECTION
SEE THAT ALL CHECKS AND DRAFTS ARE ENDORSED

	DOLLARS	CENTS
CURRENCY		
COIN		
(OUT OF TOWN, NAME CITY, IN TOWN, NAME BANK)		
CHECKS		
TOTAL $		

CENTRAL COUNTIES BANK

DIRECT LOAN APPLICATION

DATE	AMT. REQUESTED	TERM	PURPOSE	DEALER-SOURCE	

NAME:	LAST	FIRST	MIDDLE	AGE	☐ WIFE'S	☐ HUSBAND'S NAME	AGE

ADDRESS:	NO. & STREET	CITY	COUNTY	STATE	ZIP CODE	YRS. OF RESIDENCE

FORMER ADDRESS:	NO. & STREET	CITY	COUNTY	STATE	ZIP CODE	YRS. OF RESIDENCE

☐ MARRIED ☐ SINGLE	IF ☐ WIDOWED ☐ SEPARATED ☐ DIVORCED	INDICATE FROM WHOM:	HOME PHONE	NO. DEPEND.	SOCIAL SECURITY NO.	DRAFT CL.

PRESENT EMPLOYER:		INCOME	☐ WEEKLY ☐ BI-WEEKLY ☐ MONTHLY	NO. YRS. THERE

ADDRESS:	NO. & STREET	CITY	STATE	BADGE NO.	BUSINESS PHONE

POSITION	WIFE'S EMPLOYER OR OTHER INCOME	POSITION	INCOME	☐ WEEKLY ☐ BI-WEEKLY ☐ MONTHLY	NO. YRS. THERE

FORMER EMPLOYER	ADDRESS	NO. YEARS THERE

☐ CHECKING ☐ SAVINGS	BANK		BRANCH	

☐ RENT ☐ MORTGAGE	MONTHLY PAYMENT	TO WHOM PAID	ADDRESS	ORIGINAL MTG.	UNPAID BALANCE

MAKE OF AUTO	YEAR	TO WHOM INDEBTED	ADDRESS	BALANCE	PAYMENTS

LIST ALL EXISTING AND PAID OBLIGATIONS, INSTALLMENT ACCOUNTS AND DEBTS TO BANKS, FINANCE COMPANIES, STORES, ETC.

TO WHOM INDEBTED (NAME)	INDICATE: BRANCH - IF BANK; ADDRESS - IF OTHER	UNPAID BALANCE	MONTHLY PAYMENTS

NAME OF NEAREST RELATIVE NOT LIVING WITH YOU	ADDRESS

HUSBAND'S SIGNATURE	WIFE'S SIGNATURE

☐ CREDIT BUREAU   ☐ CENTRAL FILE   ☐ PROPERTY REPORT   ☐ EMPLOYMENT VERIFICATION

TYPE	TO WHOM PAID	DATE OPENED	HIGH CREDIT	TERMS	DATE PAID OR UNPAID BALANCE	RATING
MORTGAGE						
AUTOMOBILE						
OTHER						

INVESTIGATED BY_____

LOAN APPLICATIONS

db central counties bank

RESIDENTIAL LOAN APPLICATION

MORTGAGE APPLIED FOR ➤	Mortgage Amount $_____	Interest Rate %	No. of Months	Monthly Payment Principal & Interest $_____	Escrow/Impounds (to be collected monthly) ☐ Taxes ☐ Hazard Ins. ☐ PMI ☐ Other

Prepayment Option

SUBJECT PROPERTY

Property Street Address	City	County	State	Zip	No. Units

Legal Description (Attach description if necessary)	Property is ☐ Fee ☐ Leasehold ☐ Condominium ☐ Planned Unit Development

Purpose of Loan: ☐ Purchase ☐ Construction-Perm ☐ Construction ☐ Refinance ☐ Other (Explain)

Complete this line if house was just constructed on own lot . . . ☞	Year Lot Acquired	Cost of Lot $	Cost of Improvements $	Total Cost $	RE-ENTER AS PURCHASE PRICE IN DETAILS OF ☞ FINANCING

If existing liens being refinanced . . .	Purpose of Refinance	Describe Improvements [ ] made [ ] to be made

Year Built	Year Acquired	Total Investment in Prop. $

Title Will Vest in What Names?	Title will be ☐ In Joint Tenancy ☐ Other _____

BORROWER'S

Borrower	Age	Yrs. School	Co-Borrower*	Age	Yrs. School

Present Mailing Address of Borrowers	Home Phone	Business Phone	Marital Status	Years Married	Military Status

	Dependents other than Spouse		(Check One)**
	Number	Ages	☐ American Indian ☐ Spanish American ☐ Negro/Black ☐ Other Minority ☐ Oriental ☐ White (Non-minority)

Years at this Address — —

GROSS MONTHLY INCOME		HOUSING COST MONTHLY	PREVIOUS	PROPOSED	DETAILS OF PURCHASE/FINANCING	
Base earnings (Borrower)	$	Rent	$		a. Purchase price (or) Refinance Amount	$
Overtime		First Mortgage (P&I)		$	b. Repairs & Improvements	
Bonuses and Commissions		Secondary Financing (P&I)			c. Total Closing Costs	
Dividends and Interest		Hazard Insurance			d. Pre Paid Escrows	
Real Estate (Net From Schedule)		Taxes (Real Estate)			e. Total (a + b + c + d)	$
Other (Amt. from Schedule Below)		Assessments (Due or Pending)			f. First Mortgage (Amt this Loan)	( )
Subtotal (Borrower)	$	Private Mortgage Insurance			g. Other Financing	( )
Base earnings (Co-Borrower)		Total Monthly Pmt.	$	$	h. Deposit to Date	( )
Other		Utilities			i. Closing costs paid by Seller	( )
Subtotal (Co-Borrower)		Dues (Homeowners Assn.)			j. Cash required for closing	$
Total Income		Total	$	$		

BORROWER'S PRIMARY EMPLOYMENT		CO—BORROWER'S EMPLOYMENT	
Name and Address of Employer	How many years has applicant been employed in this line of work or profession? _____ years	Name and Address of Employer	How many years has applicant been employed in this line of work or profession? _____ years
	Years on this job		Years on this job
☐ Self Employed***		☐ Self Employed***	
Position/Title	Type of Business	Employers Phone No.	Position/Title	Type of Business	Employers Phone No.

LIST PREVIOUS CREDIT REFERENCES

Owed To (Name and Address)	Account Number	Purpose	Highest Balance	Date Paid
			$	

QUESTIONS APPLY TO BOTH BORROWERS

(If Yes, explain on attached sheet)   Yes or No   Yes or No

	Yes or No			Yes or No	
Have you ever taken bankruptcy?	_____		Have you owned a home before?	_____	$_____ (Market Value)
Any outstanding judgments?	_____ $_____		Do you have health and accident insurance?	_____	
Co-Maker or endorser on any notes?	_____ $_____		Do you have major medical coverage?	_____	
Defendant/Participant in a Law Suit?	_____ $_____		Do you intend to occupy property?	_____	
Obligated for child support or alimony payments?	_____ $_____		Will this property be your primary residence?	_____	

Are you an officer or partner in any other venture than listed under primary employment or other income?   YES OR NO _____

*NOTE: CO-BORROWERS not related by marriage require separate applications.
**This information is requested in accordance with suggestion of the U.S. Civil Rights Commission to protect the civil rights of all borrowers, in accordance with the intent of the United States Constitution, the Housing Act of 1949, and the Civil Rights Act of 1964 and 1968.
***Self-employed must furnish verification of income by providing a signed copy of most recent Federal Tax Return or audited Profit and Loss Statements.

NAME_____ DATE _____

LOAN APPLICATIONS

ASSETS		LIABILITIES & PLEDGED ASSETS		
Description	Cash or Market Value	Owed To (Name, Address and Account Number)	Mo. Pmt. and Mos. left to pay	Unpaid Balance
Cash Toward Purchase held by		**Indicate by(*) which will be satisfied upon sale or upon refinancing of subject property**		
		Installment Debt	$ (Mos.)	$
Checking and Savings Accounts ****				
Stocks and Bonds *No./description*				
		Loans/Pledges Against Stocks or Bonds		
Life Insurance Net Cash Value *Face Amount (S)*				
SUBTOTAL LIQUID ASSETS	$	Real Estate (itemized)		
Real Estate Owned *(Enter Total from Col 1 - Real Estate Schedule)*				
Vested Interest in Retirement Fund				
Net Worth of Business Owned *** (ATTACH FINANCIAL STATEMENT)		Other Debt (itemized)		
Auto (Make and Year)				
Furniture		Alimony and Child Support Payments		
Other Assets (itemized)		TOTAL MONTHLY PAYMENTS	C. $	
TOTAL ASSETS	A. $	NET WORTH (A.—B.) $	TOTAL LIABILITIES	B. $

SCHEDULE OF REAL ESTATE OWNED (If Additional Properties Owned Attach Separate Schedule)

Address of Property (Indicate S if Sold or PS if Pending Sale)	Type of Property	Present Market Value (1)	Amount of Mortgages & Liens	Gross Income	Mortgage Payments	Taxes, Ins., Upkeep & Misc.	Net Income
TOTALS ⟶							

AGREEMENT: The undersigned hereby applies for and agrees to accept the loan described herein, to be secured by a first mortgage or trust deed on the property described herein and represents that no part of said premises will be used for any purpose forbidden by law or restriction and that all statements made in this application are true and made for the purpose of obtaining the loan. Verification may be obtained from any source named herein.

I fully understand that it is a federal crime punishable by fine or imprisonment or both to knowingly make any false statements concerning any of the above facts, as applicable under the provisions of Title 18, United States Code, Section 1014.

Signature _____   Signature _____

(Borrower)   Date   (Co-Borrower)   Date

CCB MASTERCARD/VISA/SILENT PARTNER/ALL HOURS BANK APPLICATION

If you already have MasterCard and/or Visa please indicate your Account No and name of bank (PLEASE PRINT OR TYPE)					Your Social Security Number

Last Name	First Name	Middle Initial	Age	Telephone No	No of Dependents

Street Address	City	State	Zip Code	How Long Have You Lived Here?

Own ☐ Buying ☐ Rent ☐	Home Financed by or Rent from	Amount of Monthly Payment

Your Previous Address	City	State	Zip Code	How Long Did You Live There?

Name of Your Employer	Your Employer's Complete Address (Street, City, State, Zip Code)

Your Position	How Long Employed Here?	Your Monthly Income	Your Business Telephone

Your Previous Employer	Complete Address of Previous Employer (Street, City, State, Zip Code)	How Long Employed There?

Other Monthly Income	Optional Question: Is applicant relying on alimony, child support or maintenance payments as a basis for repayment of the credit requested? If "Yes," what is monthly amount? $_____

Name of Nearest Relative NOT Living With You	Their Complete Address (Street, City, State, Zip Code)	Relationship	Telephone Number, Area Code

CREDIT REFERENCES . . .

NAME	ADDRESS (STREET, CITY, STATE, ZIP)	ACCOUNT NUMBER	BALANCE	MO PMT
Automobile Financed With				
Credit Cards				
Other Credit References (List All Obligations)				

Your Checking Account is With	Your Checking Account No	Your Savings Account is With	Your Savings Account No

IF YOUR SPOUSE WILL BE A CO-APPLICANT OR USER OF THIS ACCOUNT, PLEASE FILL IN INFORMATION BELOW CONCERNING YOUR SPOUSE

Spouse's Full Name	Name of Spouse's Employer	Full Address of Spouse's Employer (Street, City, State, Zip Code)
Spouse's Position	How Long Employed Here?	Amount of Monthly Income	Spouse's Social Security Number

---

SEARS, ROEBUCK AND CO. INDIVIDUAL CREDIT ACCOUNT APPLICATION
Application to be completed in name of person in which the Account is to be carried.

Courtesy titles optional: ☐ Mr ☐ Mrs. ☐ Ms. ☐ Miss ☐ Other_____ PLEASE PRINT	SOC. SEC NO

First Name	Middle Initial	Last Name	AGE	Are you a United States citizen? ☐ Yes ☐ No

Street Address	Apt #	NUMBER OF DEPENDENTS

City	State	Zip Code	PHONE NO (HOME)

If others are authorized to buy on the account, print names here: 1	Relationship to applicant

HOW LONG AT PRESENT ADDRESS	☐ OWN ☐ BOARD ☐ RENT	MONTHLY RENT OR MORTGAGE PAYMENTS

FORMER ADDRESS (IF LESS THAN 2 YEARS AT PRESENT ADDRESS)	HOW LONG

EMPLOYER	BUSINESS PHONE NO

ADDRESS	CITY	STATE	ZIP

HOW LONG	OCCUPATION	TAKE HOME PAY	☐ MONTHLY ☐ WEEKLY

FORMER EMPLOYER (IF LESS THAN 1 YEAR WITH PRESENT EMPLOYER)	HOW LONG

OTHER INCOME IF ANY AMOUNT $	Note: "Alimony, child support or maintenance income need not be revealed if you do not wish to have it considered as a basis for paying this obligation."	SOURCE OF OTHER INCOME

NAME OF BANK ☐ CHECKING

ADDRESS	CITY

NAME OF BANK ☐ SAVINGS

ADDRESS	CITY

CREDIT REFERENCES

NAME AND ADDRESS

ACCOUNT NUMBER	BALANCE	MONTHLY PAYMENT

NAME OF RELATIVE OR PERSONAL REFERENCE NOT LIVING AT ABOVE ADDRESS

ADDRESS

Finance charges not in excess of those permitted by law will be charged on outstanding balances from month to month.

FORD MOTOR CREDIT COMPANY CUSTOMER STATEMENT

Ford Motor Credit Company

CUSTOMER STATEMENT (Please Print)

A P P L I C A N T

LAST NAME, FIRST NAME, MIDDLE INITIAL	AGE	SEX ☐ M ☐ F	NO. OF DEP.

PRESENT ADDRESS (NUMBER AND STREET)	CITY	STATE	ZIP CODE	COUNTY

PHONE NUMBER	LISTED IN FAM. NAME ☐ YES ☐ NO	☐ MARRIED ☐ SINGLE ☐ DIVORCED ☐ SEPARATED ☐ WIDOWED	SPOUSE'S FIRST NAME	AGE

☐ OWN HOME ☐ BUYING HOME ☐ OWN/BUYING MOBILE HOME ☐ LIVING WITH RELATIVES ☐ RENTING/LEASING   LIVED THERE YEARS ____ MONTHS ____   DRAFT STATUS OR CLASSIFICATION ____   IN RESERVES ☐ YES ☐ NO

COLLEGE GRADUATE? ☐ YES ☐ NO   IF YES, NAME OF SCHOOL ____ AND   YEAR GRADUATED ____   DEGREE(S) RECEIVED ____

NAME AND ADDRESS OF LANDLORD OR MORTGAGE HOLDER	RENT OR MORTGAGE PMT. $

PREVIOUS ADDRESS (STREET, CITY AND STATE)	LIVED THERE YRS.	YRS. IN AREA YRS.

IF VEHICLE IS PRINCIPALLY GARAGED AT OTHER THAN RESIDENCE ADDRESS:

STREET ADDRESS	CITY	STATE	CAR WILL BE PARKED ☐ GARAGE ☐ DRIVEWAY ☐ STREET

E M P L O Y M E N T

NAME AND ADDRESS OF CURRENT EMPLOYER

APPLICANT'S OCCUPATION	TIME ON JOB YRS. MOS.	EMPLOYER'S PHONE NUMBER	APPROX. MO. INCOME $

SUPERVISOR'S NAME	SOC. SEC. NO. (IF MILITARY, RANK & SERIAL NO.)	BADGE/DEPT. NO.	UNION OR LOCAL NO.	

PREVIOUS EMPLOYER'S NAME	TIME ON PREVIOUS JOB YEARS	PREVIOUS EMPLOYER'S ADDRESS	

SOURCE OF OTHER INCOME	OTHER MO. INCOME $

SPOUSE'S EMPLOYER	BUSINESS PHONE NUMBER	TIME ON JOB YEARS	SPOUSE'S MO. INCOME $

C R E D I T   D A T A

BANK REFERENCE (AND BRANCH)	☐ SAVINGS & CHECKING ☐ CHECKING ONLY ☐ SAVINGS ONLY ☐ NO ACCOUNT	COMB. MO. INCOME $

NAME AND ADDRESS OF APPLICANT'S NEAREST RELATIVE NOT IN HOUSEHOLD	PHONE NO.	RELATIONSHIP

NAME AND ADDRESS OF SPOUSE'S NEAREST RELATIVE NOT IN HOUSEHOLD	PHONE NO.	RELATIONSHIP

ACTIVE CREDIT CARDS	OIL COMPANY NAME AND CARD NUMBER	NATIONAL COMPANY NAME AND CARD NUMBER

CREDITOR'S NAME AND ADDRESS OR BRANCH	DATE OPENED	HIGH CREDIT	NO. OF INSTALMENTS AND MONTHLY PAYMENTS	DATE OF LAST PAYMENT	UNPAID BALANCE	HOW PAID
(1) (PREVIOUS CAR FINANCED BY)			@			
(2)			@			
(3)			@			

HAVE YOU EVER HAD A CAR OR OTHER MERCH. REPOSSESSED? ☐ NO ☐ YES, WHEN?   MONTH ____ YEAR ____ /   HAVE YOU OR YOUR SPOUSE EVER FILED BANKRUPTCY? ☐ NO ☐ YES, WHEN   MONTH ____ YEAR ____ /

NAME AND ADDRESS OF REGISTERED OWNER (IF NOT APPLICANT)

I N S U R A N C E

AUTOMOBILE PHYSICAL DAMAGE INSURANCE — Your Time Sale Contract will require that you procure and maintain insurance, protecting both your interest and Seller's interest against fire, theft and accidental physical damage to the vehicle, including deductible collision, except in certain states, in the case of older model used passenger cars where the unpaid cash balance is less than an amount specified by law. You may arrange for such insurance through the person of your choice, or, if you prefer, seller will attempt to obtain it on your behalf. Please indicate your preference.   ☐ I request seller to attempt to obtain such insurance on my behalf. Please complete insurance statement to assist seller in obtaining same.

☐ I WILL PROCURE SUCH INSURANCE THROUGH:
COMPANY NAME
POLICY NUMBER

AGENT'S NAME	PHONE NUMBER
ADDRESS	

I PREFER MY PAYMENTS TO COME DUE ON THE ____ OF THE MONTH

FOR THE PURPOSE OF SECURING CREDIT FROM YOU, I MADE THE ABOVE REPRESENTATIONS AND I CERTIFY THAT THE ABOVE INFORMATION IS TRUE AND COMPLETE TO THE BEST OF MY KNOWLEDGE

SIGNATURE X ____ DATE ____

CREDIT UNION APPLICATIONS

A

Book Number	NAME (to be filled in by treasurer)	Tax Iden. or Soc. Sec. No._____

| (last name) | (first name) | (middle name or initial) |

Residence
P. O. Address _____

Previous Address or
change in Address _____

Occupation _____ Division or Department _____ Tel. No._____

Date of Birth _____ Wifes first and maiden name or husbands full name _____

I hereby make application for membership in the credit union named below, and agree to conform to its bylaws and amendments thereof, copies of which have been made available to me, and to subscribe for at least one (1) share. If Life Savings insurance is carried in connection with my account, I agree, in consideration of the credit union carrying such insurance, that any designation or change of beneficiary made by me shall only be binding upon the credit union. if I have filed with the credit union prior to my death, such designation or change of beneficiary, in writing, signed by me, on the form supplied by the credit union; and, in the absence of so filing a designation or change of beneficiary, I agree on behalf of myself, my heirs, etc., to indemnify and save harmless the credit union from all loss or damage by reason of the payment of the proceeds of such insurance to such person as the credit union records show to be entitled thereto.

SIGNATURE _____ Date: _____

_____ Credit Union

This application approved by the Board; Executive Committee; or Membership Officer

Date: _____ Signed _____
Secretary; Executive Committee Member; or Membership Officer.
Cross out 2 designations in each of the two lines above not applicable.

TO BE COMPLETED BY TREAS.	
SHARE BALANCE _____	
LOAN BALANCE _____	
LOAN STATUS _____	

_____ Credit Union

APPLICATION FOR LOAN

Account No. _____
Note No. _____
Soc. Sec. No. _____

I hereby apply for a loan of $_____ for a period of _____ weeks months, to be repaid in _____

weekly
bi-weekly
semi-monthly
monthly
installments of $_____ each plus interest; I prefer the first payment to fall due on _____

I desire this loan for the following purpose (explain fully): _____

_____

Comakers or security offered _____

I hereby certify that all statements made, including those on the reverse side hereof, are true and complete and submitted for the purpose of obtaining credit.

_____ _____ Address _____
Date Signature of Applicant City _____ State _____

Information below, including appropriate signature (s), is to be filled in by **either** the credit committee or loan officer, depending upon who acts upon this application.

On _____, 19____, (I) (We) approved a loan in the amount and on the conditions requested by the above applicant, except as follows (list any changes in amount, terms, or conditions): _____

Approved by CREDIT COMMITTEE:	Approved by LOAN OFFICER:
_____	
_____	
_____	

(All committee members shown as present in the minutes of the meeting at which this application was approved must sign above.)

B

APPLICANT'S STATEMENT	COMAKER'S STATEMENT

COMAKER'S STATEMENT: NAME OF COMAKER _____ ADDRESS _____

I AM INDEBTED TO THE FOLLOWING CREDITORS (LIST ALL DEBTS SUCH AS DOCTOR BILLS. INSTALLMENTS. LOANS. REAL ESTATE MORTGAGES. ETC. ATTACH ADDITIONAL SHEET IF NECESSARY):

CREDITOR	ADDRESS	MO. PAYMENT	AMT OWING		CREDITOR	ADDRESS	MO PAYMENT	AMT OWING
HOME		$	$		HOME		$	$
AUTO		$	$		AUTO		$	$
OTHER		$	$		OTHER		$	$
		$	$				$	$
		$	$				$	$
		$	$				$	$

EMPLOYED BY	ADDRESS		EMPLOYED BY	ADDRESS
YEARS EMPLOYED	POSITION		YEARS EMPLOYED	POSITION
CLOCK OR PAYROLL NO.	SALARY $ ____ PER ____	BUS PHONE	CLOCK OR PAYROLL NO	SALARY $ ____ PER ____	BUS PHONE
DATE OF BIRTH	HOME PHONE	NAME OF SPOUSE	DATE OF BIRTH	HOME PHONE	NAME OF SPOUSE
SPOUSE EMPLOYED BY	SALARY $ ____ PER ____	DEPENDENTS, NO	SPOUSE EMPLOYED BY	SALARY $ ____ PER ____	DEPENDENTS, NO
OTHER INCOME $ ____ PER ____	SOURCE		OTHER INCOME $ ____ PER ____	SOURCE
AUTO(S) OWNED, MAKE	YEAR	MODEL	AUTO(S) OWNED, MAKE	YEAR	MODEL
OWN RESIDENCE—MARKET VALUE $ / RENT RESIDENCE—MONTHLY RENTAL $			OWN RESIDENCE—MARKET VALUE $ / RENT RESIDENCE—MONTHLY RENTAL $		
REFERENCES			REFERENCES		
OTHER PERTINENT INFORMATION			I CERTIFY THAT THE ABOVE STATEMENTS ARE TRUE AND COMPLETE.

(DATE) _____ (SIGNATURE OF COMAKER) _____

Form **W-4**
(Rev. October 1979)

Department of the Treasury—Internal Revenue Service

Employee's Withholding Allowance Certificate

Print your full name ▶

| Your social security number ▶

Address (including ZIP code) ▶

Marital status: ☐ Single ☐ Married ☐ Married, but withhold at higher Single rate

Note: *If married, but legally separated, or spouse is a nonresident alien, check the single block.*

1 Total number of allowances you are claiming (from line F of the worksheet on page 2) . . . .

2 Additional amount, if any, you want deducted from each pay (if your employer agrees) . . . . $

3 I claim exemption from withholding because (see instructions and check boxes below that apply):

a ☐ Last year I did not owe any Federal income tax and had a right to a full refund of **ALL** income tax withheld, **AND**

b ☐ This year I do not expect to owe any Federal income tax and expect to have a right to a full refund of **ALL** income tax withheld. If both

a and b apply, enter "EXEMPT" here . . . . ▶

c If you entered "EXEMPT" on line 3b, are you a full-time student? . . . . ☐ Yes ☐ No

Under the penalties of perjury, I certify that I am entitled to the number of withholding allowances claimed on this certificate, or if claiming exemption from withholding, that I am entitled to claim the exempt status.

Employee's signature ▶

Date ▶ , 19

Employer's name and address (including ZIP code) **(FOR EMPLOYER'S USE ONLY)**

Employer identification number

A57-58 Revised 1/74   SPECIAL OFFICIAL APPLICATION FOR MEMBERSHIP   PRINTED IN U.S.A.

INTERNATIONAL UNION, UNITED AUTOMOBILE, AEROSPACE & AGRICULTURAL IMPLEMENT
WORKERS OF AMERICA (UAW)
DETROIT, MICHIGAN 48214   Date_____

Name_____   L. U. No._____
(Print)

Address_____ City_____ State_____ Zip_____

Dept._____ Social Security No._____

I hereby designate, select and empower the International Union, United Automobile, Aerospace and Agricultural Implement Workers of America (UAW), its agents or representatives, to act for me as my exclusive representative for the purposes of collective bargaining in respect to rates of pay, wages, hours of employment or other conditions of employment, and to enter into contracts with my employer covering all such matters, including contracts requiring the continuance of my membership in said Union as a condition of my employment or continued employment, and contracts requiring the employer to deduct, collect, or assist in collecting from my wages or a regular supplemental unemployment benefit payable under its supplemental unemployment benefit plan any dues and fees payable to said Union; and I hereby revoke every selection or designation which in any manner may heretofore have been made by me, of any other representative for any of such purposes.

I further irrevocably designate, authorize and empower the said Union exclusively to appear and act for me and in my behalf before any board, court, committee or other tribunal in any matter affecting my status as an employee, or as a member of said Union, and exclusively to act as my agent to represent and bind me in the presentation, prosecution, adjustment and settlement of all grievances, complaints or disputes of any kind or character arising out of the employer-employee relationship as fully and to all intents and purposes as I might or could do if personally present.

I pledge my honor to faithfully observe the Constitution and laws of this Union and the Constitution of the United States (or the Dominion of Canada as the case may be); to comply with all the rules and regulations for the government thereof; not to divulge or make known any private proceedings of this Union; to faithfully perform all the duties assigned to me to the best of my ability and skill; to so conduct myself at all times as not to bring reproach upon my Union, and at all times to bear true and faithful allegiance to the International Union, United Automobile, Aerospace and Agricultural Implement Workers of America (UAW).

(Applicant's Signature)_____

(Witness)_____

AUTHORIZATION FOR CHECK-OFF OF DUES

TO THE_____COMPANY   Date_____

I hereby assign to Local Union No._____, International Union, United Automobile, Aerospace and Agricultural Implement Workers of America (UAW), from any wages earned or to be earned by me or a regular supplemental unemployment benefit payable under its supplemental unemployment benefit plan as your employee (in my present or in any future employment by you), such sums as the Financial

Officer of said Local Union No._____may certify as due and owing from me as membership dues, including an initiation or reinstatement fee and monthly dues in such sum as may be established from time to time as union dues in accordance with the Constitution of the International Union, UAW. I authorize and direct you to deduct such amounts from my pay and to remit same to the Union at such times and in such manner as may be agreed upon between you and the Union at any time while this authorization is in effect.

This assignment, authorization and direction shall be irrevocable for the period of one (1) year from the date of delivery hereof to you, or until the termination of the collective agreement between the Company and the Union which is in force at the time of delivery of this authorization, whichever occurs sooner; and I agree and direct that this assignment, authorization and direction shall be automatically renewed, and shall be irrevocable for successive periods of one (1) year each or for the period of each succeeding applicable collective agreement between the Company and the Union, whichever shall be shorter, unless written notice is given by me to the Company and the Union, not more than twenty (20) days and not less than ten (10) days prior to the expiration of each period of one (1) year, or of each applicable collective agreement between the Company and the Union whichever occurs sooner.

This authorization is made pursuant to the provisions of Section 302(c) of the Labor Management Relations Act of 1947 and otherwise.

_____   _____
(Signature of Employee here)   (Address of Employee)

_____   _____
(Type or print name of Employee here)   (City)   (State)   (Zip)

_____
(Date of Sign.)   (Emp. Clock No.)   (Soc. Sec. No.)   (Date of Del. to Employer)

CONFIDENTIAL
APPLICATION FOR EMPLOYMENT
WITH
BLUE CROSS AND BLUE SHIELD OF NORTH CAROLINA
P. O. BOX 2291, DURHAM, N. C. 27702

BCBSNC DOES NOT DISCRIMINATE BECAUSE OF AGE, SEX, RELIGION, RACE, COLOR, AND NATIONAL ORIGIN AND ENGAGES IN AFFIRMATIVE ACTION IN HIRING MINORITIES, THE HANDICAPPED, AND VETERANS.

PLEASE PRINT IN BLUE OR BLACK INK OR TYPE

PERSONAL DATA

NAME: LAST	FIRST	MIDDLE	MAIDEN NAME	PREFERRED NAME

PRESENT ADDRESS: STREET	CITY	STATE	ZIP CODE	HOW LONG?

SOCIAL SECURITY NUMBER	HOME TELEPHONE NUMBER AREA CODE: ( )	BUSINESS OR OTHER TELEPHONE NUMBER

IN CASE OF EMERGENCY, PLEASE CONTACT (NAME, TELEPHONE NUMBER)

YOUR JOB REQUIREMENTS

TYPE OF WORK DESIRED (PLEASE GIVE NATURE OF WORK OR POSITION TITLE): | MINIMUM ACCEPTABLE SALARY:

HOW SOON COULD YOU BE AVAILABLE IF AN EMPLOYMENT OFFER IS EXTENDED? | WORK LOCATION (CITY) DESIRED:

CHECK APPROPRIATE BLOCK FOR TYPE OF EMPLOYEMENT DESIRED:

☐ FULL-TIME ☐ PART-TIME ☐ TEMPORARY ☐ SUMMER

GENERAL INFORMATION

DO YOU HAVE ANY PHYSICAL, MENTAL OR MEDICAL IMPAIRMENT OR DISABILITY THAT WOULD LIMIT YOUR JOB PERFORMANCE FOR THE POSITION FOR WHICH YOU ARE APPLYING? ☐ YES ☐ NO

IF YES, PLEASE EXPLAIN _____

HAVE YOU FILED AN APPLICATION HERE BEFORE? ☐ NO ☐ YES, DATE: _____

HAVE YOU EVER BEEN CONVICTED OF A CRIMINAL OFFENSE? ☐ YES ☐ NO

IF YES, PLEASE BRIEFLY DESCRIBE THE CIRCUMSTANCES OF YOUR CONVICTION(S) INCLUDING CHARGE(S), LOCATION(S), DATE(S), AND DISPOSITION(S). NOTE: REPORT ALL OFFENSES OF ANY NATURE WHERE THE CONVICTION INVOLVED A FINE OF MORE THAN $200.00 OR IMPRISONMENT. DO NOT INCLUDE MINOR TRAFFIC OFFENSES.

_____

_____

_____

HAVE YOU EVER BEEN DENIED BOND? ☐ YES ☐ NO IF YES, PLEASE EXPLAIN:

_____

_____

BY WHOM OR HOW WERE YOU REFERRED TO BCBSNC?

LIST ANY RELATIVES EMPLOYED BY BCBSNC:

NAME _____ RELATIONSHIP TO YOU _____ DEPARTMENT _____

NAME _____ RELATIONSHIP TO YOU _____ DEPARTMENT _____

FOR EQUAL OPPORTUNITY STATISTICAL REPORTING PURPOSES ONLY, PLEASE PROVIDE THE FOLLOWING INFORMATION.

DATE OF BIRTH:			ETHNIC BACKGROUND:	
MO.	DAY	YEAR		

ETHNIC BACKGROUND: ☐ AMERICAN INDIAN ☐ BLACK ☐ ORIENTAL
☐ SPANISH HERITAGE ☐ WHITE ☐ OTHER _____

PLEASE CHECK IF ANY OF THE FOLLOWING ARE APPLICABLE: ☐ VIETNAM ERA VETERAN ☐ DISABLED VET ☐ HANDICAPPED INDIVIDUAL

PLEASE CHECK IF YOU ARE: ☐ 18 OR UNDER (INDICATE AGE _____) ☐ 65 OR OLDER ☐ FEMALE ☐ MALE

U.S. CITIZEN ☐ YES ☐ NO IF NO, INDICATE TYPE OF VISA _____ ☐ MARRIED

U.S. VETERAN ☐ YES ☐ NO IF YES, INDICATE DATE OF SEPARATION _____ ☐ SINGLE

NAME_____ DATE _____

NOTE: EVEN IF YOU ARE SUBMITTING A RESUME, PLEASE COMPLETE THE SECTIONS BELOW IN FULL.

- -

SKILLS

DO NOT COMPLETE THIS SECTION IF YOU ARE APPLYING FOR A POSITION THAT DOES NOT REQUIRE CLERICAL OR TECHNICAL SKILLS.

TYPING_____CORRECT WORDS PER MINUTE

SHORTHAND_____CORRECT WORDS PER MINUTE

DICTAPHONE _____CORRECT WORDS PER MINUTE

LIST THE DATA PROCESSING EQUIPMENT YOU OPERATE AND/OR PROGRAMMING LANGUAGES YOU WRITE.

KEYPUNCH_____STROKES PER HOUR_____

OTHER: _____

_____

OTHER OFFICE SKILLS AND/OR OFFICE OR PRINTING EQUIPMENT YOU OPERATE:

_____

_____

_____

_____

_____

EDUCATION AND TRAINING   (PLEASE COMPLETE ALL APPROPRIATE SECTIONS)

TYPE OF SCHOOL	NAME AND ADDRESS OF SCHOOL	DATES ATTENDED	CIRCLE YEARS COMPLETED		GRADUATED YES NO		TYPE OF DEGREE RECEIVED MAJOR/MINOR
HIGH SCHOOL (LAST ATTENDED)		FROM: (MO/YR) / TO: (MO/YR)	9 10 11 12		☐	☐	
VOCATIONAL AND TECHNICAL		FROM: (MO/YR) / TO: (MO/YR)	1 2 3 4		☐	☐	
JUNIOR COLLEGE		FROM: (MO/YR) / TO: (MO/YR)	1 2 3 4		☐	☐	
COLLEGE; UNIVERSITY		FROM: (MO/YR) / TO: (MO/YR)	1 2 3 4		☐	☐	
COLLEGE; UNIVERSITY		FROM: (MO/YR) / TO: (MO/YR)	1 2 3 4		☐	☐	
MILITARY TRAINING		FROM: (MO/YR) / TO: (MO/YR)	1 2 3 4		☐	☐	
EQUIVALENCY DIPLOMAS		FROM: (MO/YR) / TO: (MO/YR)	1 2 3 4		☐	☐	

NAME_____ DATE _____

EMPLOYMENT EXPERIENCE

PLEASE LIST YOUR JOB HISTORY FOR THE PAST TEN YEARS (OR THE LAST FIVE EMPLOYERS). <u>START WITH YOUR PRESENT STATUS</u> AND NOTE ANY PERIODS IN WHICH YOU WERE NOT EMPLOYED. INCLUDE U. S. MILITARY SERVICE (SHOW RANK/RATE AT DISCHARGE), PREVIOUS BCBSNC EXPERIENCE, AND SUMMER/PART-TIME/TEMPORARY JOBS.

COMPANY NAME AND ADDRESS AND SUPERVISOR'S NAME	DATES EMPLOYED MO. YR.	BASE RATE OF PAY		POSITION TITLE AND DESCRIPTION OF DUTIES	REASON FOR LEAVING
COMPANY NAME AND ADDRESS	FROM	STARTING $	PER		
	TO	FINAL $	PER		
SUPERVISOR NAME					
COMPANY NAME AND ADDRESS	FROM	STARTING $	PER		
	TO	FINAL $	PER		
SUPERVISOR NAME					
COMPANY NAME AND ADDRESS	FROM	STARTING $	PER		
	TO	FINAL $	PER		
SUPERVISOR NAME					
COMPANY NAME AND ADDRESS	FROM	STARTING $	PER		
	TO	FINAL $	PER		
SUPERVISOR NAME					
COMPANY NAME AND ADDRESS	FROM	STARTING $	PER		
	TO	FINAL $	PER		
SUPERVISOR NAME					

DO YOU HAVE ANY OBJECTION TO OUR CONTACTING YOUR PRESENT EMPLOYER?

☐ YES ☐ NO AREA CODE _____ TELEPHONE NUMBER _____

I HEREBY CERTIFY THAT THE FACTS SET FORTH IN THIS EMPLOYMENT APPLICATION ARE TRUE AND COMPLETE TO THE BEST OF MY KNOWLEDGE. I UNDERSTAND THAT FALSIFIED STATEMENTS ON THIS APPLICATION ARE JUSTIFICATION FOR REFUSAL OF, OR IF EMPLOYED, FOR TERMINATION OF BCBSNC EMPLOYMENT.

YOU ARE HEREBY AUTHORIZED TO MAKE ANY INVESTIGATION OF MY PERSONAL HISTORY AND FINANCIAL AND CREDIT RECORD THROUGH ANY INVESTIGATIVE OR CREDIT AGENCIES OR BUREAUS OF YOUR CHOICE.

APPLICANT SIGNATURE_____DATE _____

I HEREBY AUTHORIZE THIS ORGANIZATION, AND ALSO AUTHORIZE AND REQUEST EACH FORMER EMPLOYER OR PERSON GIVEN AS A REFERENCE, TO ANSWER ALL QUESTIONS THAT MAY BE ASKED, AND TO GIVE INFORMATION THAT MAY BE REQUESTED IN CONNECTION WITH THIS APPLICATION, OR CONCERNING ME OR MY WORK, HABITS, CHARACTER, OR SKILL.

APPLICANT SIGNATURE _____DATE_____

IF YOU ARE INTERESTED IN SPEAKING WITH ONE OF OUR EMPLOYMENT INTERVIEWERS FOR A BRIEF (5-10 MINUTE 'GET-ACQUAINTED' ONLY) INTERVIEW, PLEASE BRING THIS APPLICATION WITH YOU TO THE BLUE CROSS AND BLUE SHIELD OF NORTH CAROLINA LOBBY THIS COMING THURSDAY MORNING BETWEEN 8:30 A.M. AND 11:00 A.M. IF THIS IS NOT CONVENIENT FOR YOU, PLEASE LEAVE YOUR APPLICATION WITH THE RECEPTIONIST OR MAIL IT TO US.

APPLICATION FOR EMPLOYMENT—STATE BUREAU OF EMPLOYMENT SECURITY

A	B	C	D	E	F	G	H	I	J	1	2	3	4	5	6	7	8	9	10	11	12

TITLES | **CODES**

1. PRINT LAST NAME BELOW — FIRST — MIDDLE INITIAL

2. ADDRESS NUMBER AND STREET, R.D. OR P.O. BOX NO.

CITY — STATE — ZIP CODE — 3. TELEPHONE NUMBER

SKILLS, KNOWLEDGES, ABILITIES | **DATES**

4. SEX ☐ M ☐ F

5. SOCIAL SECURITY NUMBER

6. DATE OF BIRTH — MONTH DAY YEAR — 7. HEIGHT ft. in. — 8. WEIGHT lbs.

9. ☐ SINGLE ☐ WIDOWED ☐ SEPARATED ☐ MARRIED ☐ DIVORCED

10. CIRCLE HIGHEST YEAR OF EDUCATION COMPLETED: 1 2 3 4 5 6 7 8 9 10 11 12 Grade and High School — 1 2 3 4 5 6 7 College — DEGREES RECEIVED

NAME OF COURSES OF STUDY OR TRAINING WHICH PREPARED YOU FOR WORK GIVE NAME OF SCHOOL, LENGTH OF COURSE, AND DATE COMPLETED:

TEST RESULTS

12. CHECK (✔) IF YOU HAVE: ☐ TOOLS ☐ OCCUPATIONAL LICENSE ☐ DRIVER'S LICENSE ☐ AUTOMOBILE ☐ TRUCK

13. IF UNION MEMBER, GIVE NUMBER, NAME AND AFFILIATION OF LOCAL:

COMMONWEALTH OF PENNSYLVANIA
DEPARTMENT OF LABOR AND INDUSTRY — BUREAU OF EMPLOYMENT SECURITY
ADDITIONAL APPLICATION CARD — ES-512 1-73

WORK HISTORY

15. FIRM NAME	19 NAME OF JOB	DESCRIBE WHAT YOU DID AND HOW YOU DID IT
16 ADDRESS		
17 EMPLOYER'S BUSINESS		
18. LENGTH OF JOB — DATE ENDED — PAY		REASON FOR LEAVING
20. FIRM NAME	24. NAME OF JOB	DESCRIBE WHAT YOU DID AND HOW YOU DID IT
21. ADDRESS		
22 EMPLOYER'S BUSINESS		
23. LENGTH OF JOB — DATE ENDED — PAY		REASON FOR LEAVING

COMMENTS

NAME_____ DATE _____

H105.102   REV. 11-81

PENNSYLVANIA DEPARTMENT OF HEALTH
VITAL RECORDS

If Veteran (✓)
See Other Side

APPLICATION FOR CERTIFIED COPY OF BIRTH OR DEATH RECORD

PLEASE PRINT OR TYPE   To avoid delay please complete all items.

			DO NOT WRITE IN THIS SPACE
INDICATE NUMBER OF COPIES	BIRTH $4.00 DEATH $3.00		

Date of Birth/ Or Date of Death	Place of Birth Or Place of Death County	Twp. or Borough	

| Name at Birth Or Name at Death | | SEX | File No. |
| | | | Index By │ Search By |

| Father's Name | First   Middle   Last | | Certified No. |

| Mother's Maiden Name | First   Middle   Last | | Refund Ck. No. |

| Hospital | Funeral Director | | Date — Amount |

Reason for Request (Check One): ☐ School   ☐ Marriage
☐ Passport   ☐ Other (Specify)

Postage: $

How Are You Related to This Person?

Applicant's Signature	
Applicant's	No. Street
Address	City State Zip Code
Applicant's Phone No.	Area Code Number

Prices for Certified Copies Are: Births: $4.00 each — Deaths: $3.00 each
PLEASE DO NOT SEND CASH.

Check or Money Order should be made payable to VITAL RECORDS
Please enclose self-addressed stamped envelope for return of copies.
Records available are from 1906 to the present

☐ Prev. Amend.   ☐ Adopt   ☐ Affidavit

☐ Usage   ☐ Court Order   ☐ Issue Affidavit

- -

DO NOT REMOVE THIS STUB

If birth or death occurred in: **Mail application to:**

1) **Philadelphia** — Division of Vital Records, 402 City Hall Annex, Philadelphia, Pa. 19107

2) **Pittsburgh** — Division of Vital Records, Room 512, 300 Liberty Ave., Pittsburgh, Pa. 15222

3) **Erie** — Division of Vital Records, 3832 Liberty St., Erie, Pa. 16509

4) **Scranton** — Division of Vital Records, 100 Lackawanna Ave., Scranton, Pa. 18503

Print or type your name and address in the space below.

Name
Street
City, State, Zip Code

FOR ALL OTHER AREAS
MAIL COMPLETED APPLICATION TO:
Pennsylvania Department of Health
Division of Vital Records
P.O. Box 1528
New Castle, Pa. 16103
or visit our public offices at
101 South Mercer Street, New Castle or
Room 129, Health & Welfare Bldg., Harrisburg

PRIVACY ACT STATEMENT

The Military Selective Service Act, Selective Service Regulations, and the President's Proclamation on Registration require that you provide the indicated information, including your Social Security Account Number.

The principal purpose of the required information is to establish your registration with the Selective Service System. This information may be furnished to the following agencies for the purposes stated:

Department of Defense—for exchange of information concerning registration, classification, enlistment, examination and induction of individuals.

Alternate service employers—for exchange of information with employers regarding a registrant who is a conscientious objector for the purpose of placement and supervision of performance of alternate service in lieu of induction into military service.

Department of Justice—for review and processing of suspected violations of the Military Selective Service Act, or for perjury, and for defense of a civil action arising from administrative processing under such Act.

Federal Bureau of Investigation—for location of an individual when suspected of violation of the Military Selective Service Act.

Immigration and Naturalization Service—to provide information for use in determining an individual's eligibility for re-entry into the United States.

Department of State—for determination of an alien's eligibility for possible entry into the United States and United States citizenship.

Office of Veterans' Reemployment Rights, United States Department of Labor—to assist veterans in need of information concerning reemployment rights.

General Public—Registrant's Name, Selective Service Number, Date of Birth and Classification, Military Selective Service Act Section 6, 50 U.S.C. App. 456.

Your failure to provide the required information may violate the Military Selective Service Act. Conviction of such violation may result in imprisonment for not more than five years or a fine of not more than $10,000 or both imprisonment and fine.

SELECTIVE SERVICE SYSTEM
Registration Form
READ PRIVACY ACT STATEMENT ON REVERSE
PLEASE PRINT CLEARLY

— DO NOT WRITE IN THE ABOVE SPACE —

1 DATE OF BIRTH
Name of Month / Day / Year

2 SEX ☐ MALE ☐ FEMALE

3 SOCIAL SECURITY NUMBER

4 PRINT FULL NAME
Last / First / Middle

5 CURRENT MAILING ADDRESS
Number and Street
City / State or Foreign Country / Zip Code

PERMANENT RESIDENCE (If different than BLOCK 5)

6 Number and Street
City / State or Foreign Country / Zip Code

7 CURRENT TELEPHONE NUMBER
Area Code / Number

8 I AFFIRM THE FOREGOING STATEMENTS ARE TRUE
Signature of Registrant
Today's Date

SSS FORM 1 (JAN 82) (Previous Editions Will Not Be Used And Will Be Destroyed)

Postal Date Stamp & Clerk Initials
☐ ID ☐ NO ID ☐ OTHER

OMB Approval 3240-0002

SELECTIVE SERVICE SYSTEM
Change of Information Form

— DO NOT WRITE IN THE ABOVE SPACE —

1 FULL NAME
(Last) (First) (Middle)

2 DATE OF BIRTH
(Mo) (Day) (Yr)

3 SOCIAL SECURITY NUMBER

4 SELECTIVE SERVICE NUMBER

5 CURRENT MAILING ADDRESS ON FILE
(Number) (Street) (Apt No.)
(City) (State or Foreign Country) (Zip Code)

CHANGE ☐ Name ☐ Current Mailing Address ☐ Permanent Address ☐ Telephone No.

6 FULL NAME
(Last) (First) (Middle)

7 CURRENT MAILING ADDRESS
(Number) (Street) (Apt No.)
(City) (State or Foreign Country) (Zip Code) (Telephone No.)

8 PERMANENT RESIDENCE ADDRESS
(Number) (Street) (Apt No.)
(City) (State or Foreign Country) (Zip Code) (Telephone No.)

9 TODAY'S DATE
SIGNATURE OF REGISTRANT

SSS FORM 2 (AUG 1980) (DESTROY PREVIOUS EDITIONS) OMB APPROVAL 194 R0003

APPLICATION FOR ENLISTMENT—ARMED FORCES OF THE UNITED STATES

APPLICATION FOR ENLISTMENT– ARMED FORCES OF THE UNITED STATES	FORM APPROVED OMB 22-R 0331

INSTRUCTIONS:

1. The information in this document is to determine your eligibility for enlistment in the Armed Forces of the United States. Some of the information requested is of a personal and confidential nature, and you do not have to provide such information unless you voluntarily wish to enlist in the Armed Forces of the United States. .

2. The authority to request this information is contained in Sections 504, 505, 508 and 510 of Title 10, United States Code, which prescribe qualifications for enlistment in the Armed Forces of the United States. You are required to record on this application, your answers to all questions except those in items 12, 29, 33 and 37.

3. Your answers to questions in item 37 may be given orally in a personal interview as prescribed in the instructions for that item. Failure to answer completely any of the required questions in the application may result in your being refused enlistment in the Armed Forces.

4. If your application is accepted and you are subsequently enlisted in a component of the Armed Forces of the United States, the information

provided by you on this application becomes a part of your military personnel records which are used to provide promotion, reassignment, training and other personnel management actions for you. The data is FOR OFFICIAL USE ONLY and will be maintained and used in strict confidence in accordance with Federal law and regulations.

5. Making a knowing and willful false statement on this application can be punished by fine or imprisonment or both under Section 1001 of Title 18, United States Code.

6. All information provided by you which reflects unfavorably on your past conduct and performance could have an adverse impact on you in your military career in situations such as consideration for special assignment, security clearances and court martial and administrative proceedings.

7. Type or print legibly all answers; if the answer is ''none'' or ''not applicable'', so state.

8. If additional space is needed for any answer, continue in item 41, ''Remarks''.

I. PERSONAL DATA

1. NAME (Last, first, middle (maiden, if any), Jr., Sr., etc.)	2. SOCIAL SECURITY NO.

3. HOME OF RECORD (City, County, State, Zip Code)	4. CITIZENSHIP ☐ U.S. ☐ U.S. NATIONAL ☐ NON-U.S. Specify:	5. SEX ☐ MALE ☐ FEMALE

6. RACE ☐ CAUC. ☐ NEGRO ☐ OTHER	7. ETHNIC GROUP	8. PRESENT ADDRESS (Street, City, State, County, Zip Code)

9. MARITAL STATUS	10. NUMBER OF DEPENDENTS	11. DATE OF BIRTH	12. RELIGIOUS PREFERENCE (Optional)	13. HIGHEST GRADE COMPLETED

14. SELECTIVE SERVICE SYSTEM DATA NUMBER CLASS.	15. FOREIGN LANGUAGE & SKILL _____ ☐ READ ☐ WRITE ☐ SPEAK	16. DRIVER'S LICENSE INFORMATION STATE NUMBER EXPIRES

III. VERIFICATION OF PERSONAL DATA

23. If Preferred Enlistment Name (name given in block 1) is not the same as on your birth certificate and has not been changed by legal procedure prescribed by state law, complete the following:

   a. NAME AS SHOWN ON BIRTH CERTIFICATE

I hereby state that I have not changed my name through any court procedure; and that I prefer to use the name by which I am known in the community as a matter of convenience and with no criminal or fraudulent intent. I further state that I am the same person as the one whose name is shown in block 1.

b WITNESS (Name, grade, and signature)	c. SIGNATURE OF APPLICANT

24. EDUCATION

YEAR & MONTH		NAME AND LOCATION OF SCHOOL	GRADUATE		DEGREE RECEIVED
FROM	TO		YES	NO	

25 CITIZENSHIP VERIFICATION (To be completed in presence of your recruiter).

a. PLACE OF BIRTH (City, State and (if not in USA) Country)	b. BIRTH CERTIFICATE ISSUED BY (County and State)
c. BIRTH CERTIFICATE FILE NUMBER	d. IF NATURALIZED, CERTIFICATE NO.	e. IF DERIVED, PARENTS' CERTIFICATE NO(S), DATE, PLACE AND COURT
f. IF ALIEN, ALIEN REGISTRATION NUMBER		
g. NATIVE COUNTRY	h. DATE AND PORT OF ENTRY	

APPLICATION FOR ENLISTMENT—ARMED FORCES OF THE UNITED STATES

26. MILITARY SERVICE

a. Are you now or have ever been in the Regular, Reserve or National Guard of the United States?

☐ No ☐ Yes. If "yes", complete the following:

b. PAY GRADE AND SERVICE NUMBER	c. SERVICE AND COMPONENT	d. DATE OF ENTRY	e. DATE OF DISCH	f. TYPE DISCH/REL	g. TIME LOST (NO. OF DAYS)

h. If you are now a member of a US Reserve or National Guard organization, fill in organization name and unit address:

IV. OTHER BACKGROUND DATA

28a. RELATIVES	b. DATE AND PLACE OF BIRTH	c. PRESENT ADDRESS	d. CITIZENSHIP
FATHER			
MOTHER (Maiden-name)			
SPOUSE (Maiden name)			
CHILDREN (Show Relationship)			
OTHER (specify)			

29. COMMERCIAL LIFE INSURANCE POLICIES YOU OWN ON YOUR LIFE—Optional entry; used to assist your survivors in filing claims should you die while on active duty.

a. NAME OF COMPANY ISSUING POLICY	b. POLICY NUMBER

30. RELATIVES AND ALIEN FRIENDS LIVING IN FOREIGN COUNTRIES—List anyone with whom you had or have a close relationship, who lives in a foreign country.

a. NAME AND RELATIONSHIP	b. AGE	c. OCCUPATION	d. ADDRESS	e. CITIZENSHIP

31. RESIDENCES—List all from 10th birthday.

YEAR & MONTH FROM	TO	NUMBER AND STREET	CITY	STATE	ZIP CODE

32. EMPLOYMENT—Show every employment you have had and all periods of unemployment.

a. YEAR & MONTH FROM	TO	b. Company name and address (Street, City, State, and Zip Code)	c. JOB TITLE	d. SUPERVISOR NAME

e. HAVE YOU EVER WORKED FOR A FOREIGN GOVERNMENT?

☐ No ☐ Yes If "yes", give dates of employment, government you worked for, location and nature of your duties:

33. MEMBERSHIP IN YOUTH PROGRAMS—Optional entry; you may be eligible for a higher paygrade, based on membership and participation in the youth programs listed below.

☐ No membership.

ORGANIZATION	MEMBERSHIP HELD FROM	TO	CONDUCTED BY (SPONSOR)	LOCATION (SCHOOL AND ADDRESS)	YEARS COMPLETED OR LEVEL REACHED
ROTC					(YEARS)
JROTC					(YEARS)
CAP			AIR FORCE		(LEVEL)
SEA CADET			NAVY		(LEVEL)
OTHER (Specify)					

NAME_____ DATE _____

APPLICATION FOR ENLISTMENT—ARMED FORCES OF THE UNITED STATES

34. FOREIGN TRAVEL—Other than as a direct result of military service.

YEAR & MONTH		COUNTRY VISITED	PURPOSE OF TRAVEL
FROM	TO		

35. DECLARATIONS—Explain "Yes" answers in item 41.

a. HAVE YOU EVER BEEN REJECTED FOR ENLISTMENT, REENLISTMENT, OR INDUCTION INTO ANY BRANCH OF THE ARMED FORCES OF THE UNITED STATES? ☐ NO ☐ YES	d. ARE YOU NOW DRAWING, OR DO YOU HAVE AN APPLICATION PENDING OR APPROVAL FOR, RETIRED PAY, DISABILITY ALLOWANCE, OR SEVERANCE PAY OR A PENSION FROM THE GOVERNMENT OF THE UNITED STATES? ☐ NO ☐ YES
b. ARE YOU A CONSCIENTIOUS OBJECTOR? ☐ NO ☐ YES	
c. ARE YOU NOW OR HAVE YOU EVER BEEN A DESERTER FROM ANY BRANCH OF THE ARMED FORCES OF THE UNITED STATES? ☐ NO ☐ YES	e. ARE YOU THE ONLY LIVING CHILD OF YOUR PARENTS? ☐ NO ☐ YES

36. UNDERSTANDINGS.

a. I understand that if I am rejected for enlistment because of a disqualification I have concealed, I may not be provided return transportation from the place of examination to my home.	(INITIALS)
b. (For male applicants only). I understand that if I have not reached my 26th birthday that an original enlistment obligates me to serve in the Armed Forces for a period of six (6) years (active and reserve) unless sooner discharged.	(INITIALS)

V. CERTIFICATION

42. BY APPLICANT: I UNDERSTAND THAT THE ARMED FORCES REPRESENTATIVE WHO WILL ACCEPT MY ENLISTMENT DOES SO IN RELIANCE ON THE INFORMATION PROVIDED BY ME IN THIS DOCUMENT; THAT IF ANY OF THE INFORMATION IS KNOWINGLY FALSE OR INCORRECT, I MAY BE PROSECUTED UNDER FEDERAL CIVILIAN OR MILITARY LAW OR SUBJECT TO ADMINISTRATIVE SEPARATION PROCEEDINGS AND, IN EITHER INSTANCE, I MAY RECEIVE A LESS THAN HONORABLE DISCHARGE WHICH COULD AFFECT MY FUTURE EMPLOYMENT OPPORTUNITIES. I CERTIFY THAT THE INFORMATION GIVEN BY ME IN THIS DOCUMENT IS TRUE, COMPLETE, AND CORRECT TO THE BEST OF MY KNOWLEDGE AND BELIEF.

a. DATE	b. NAME (Type or Print)	c. SIGNATURE OF APPLICANT

44. RECRUITER: I certify that I have witnessed applicant's signature above and further certify that I have verified the data in Sections I, II, III, and IV of this document, and the documents listed above as prescribed by my directives. I understand my liability to trial by courts-martial under the Uniform Code of Military Justice should I effect or cause to be effected the enlistment of anyone known by me to be ineligible for enlistment.

a. DATE	b. NAME, GRADE, SSN, AND RECRUITER ID NO. (Type or Print)	c. SIGNATURE OF RECRUITER

VI. PARENTAL/GUARDIAN CONSENT FOR ENLISTMENT

45. I/we certify that the applicant named herein has no other legal guardian than me/us and I/we consent to his/her enlistment in the _____ subject to all the requirements and lawful commands of the officers who may, from time to time, be placed over him/her; and I/we certify that no promise of any kind has been made to me/us concerning assignment to duty, or promotion during his/her enlistment as an inducement to me/us to sign this consent. I/we hereby authorized the Armed Forces representatives concerned to administer medical examinations, mental and/or aptitude testing, and conduct records checks to determine applicant's enlistment eligibility. I/we relinquish all claim to his/her service and to any wage or compensation for such service.

46. *For enlistment in a Reserve Component:* I/we understand that as a member of a Reserve Component, he/she must serve minimum periods of active duty unless excused by competent authority. In the event he/she fails to fulfill the obligations of his/her Reserve commitment, he/she may be recalled to active duty as prescribed by law. I/we further understand that while the applicant is in the Ready Reserve, he/she may be ordered to extended active duty in time of war or national emergency declared by the Congress or the President or when otherwise authorized by law.

47. I/we certify that the applicant's birth date is: _____

NAME AND SIGNATURE OF WITNESSING OFFICIAL	SIGNATURE OF PARENT OR LEGAL GUARDIAN
NAME AND SIGNATURE OF WITNESSING OFFICIAL	SIGNATURE OF PARENT OR LEGAL GUARDIAN

VERIFICATION OF SINGLE SIGNATURE CONSENT

APPLICATION FOR LIFE INSURANCE

APPLICATION FOR INSURANCE	**PART 1**	**Philadelphia Life Insurance Company** Philadelphia, Pennsylvania 19107

The Applicant hereby makes application to Philadelphia Life Insurance Company for a policy or policies of insurance and represents that the statements and answers set forth below, by whomsoever written, are full, complete and true to the best of Applicant's knowledge and belief and agrees that they shall be considered as the basis of any insurance which may be issued hereon.

COMPLETE THIS SECTION FOR ALL POLICIES

1. Print Full Name and Residence Address of Proposed Insured. ☐ M ☐ F

   First ___ Middle ___ Last

   No. ___ Street

   City and State ___ ZIP Code

2. Date of Birth | Age Nearest Birthday ___ | State of Birth | Marital Status

   Month, Day, Year

3. Occupation ___

   Other occupations ___

4. Life Insurance and Annuities in force (if none, so state)

Company	Amount	Year Issued	Acc. Death Benefit	Disability Income

   Health Insurance in force (if none, so state)

Company	Monthly Amount	Waiting Periods	Benefit Periods	Issue Date

   Total AD & D benefit carried $ ___

5. Is this insurance (or annuity) intended to replace or change insurance (or annuities) in this or any other company? Yes No (If "yes" explain under Remarks) ___ ☐ ☐

6. GENERAL INFORMATION (Include all family members to be insured.) If answered "Yes" give details under "REMARKS", and name of person to which question applies. HAS ANY PERSON proposed for coverage:

   Yes No
   a. ever been deferred, rejected or discharged from military service because of a physical or mental condition? ___ ☐ ☐
   b. ever requested or received a pension, benefits, or payment because of an injury, sickness or disability? ___ ☐ ☐
   c. contemplated flying or flown as pilot, student pilot or crew member during the last two years? (If "yes," complete Aviation Supplement.) ___ ☐ ☐
   d. had any application or policy for life or health insurance declined, special rated, restricted, postponed, canceled or reinstatement denied? ___ ☐ ☐
   e. currently applied for or had a life or health application pending in any other company? ___ ☐ ☐

   REMARKS:

7. Beneficiary: Print full names and relationship to Proposed Insured.

   Contingent Beneficiary, if any

   Does owner reserve right to change beneficiary? ☐ Yes ☐ No

8. Owner: Print name, address and relationship if other than Proposed Insured.

9. Total amount of premium submitted herewith $ ___
   Indicate premium allocation:
   Life $ ___ Accident & Sickness $ ___ Annuity $ ___

COMPLETE THIS SECTION FOR POLICY OF LIFE INSURANCE

10. Life Insurance Applied For (Use Ratebook Description)

    Amount $ ___ Plan ___
    Basic Plan Only ___ No. of Years
    ☐ Non-Participating ☐ Participating

    Additional Riders
    ☐ Supp. Term $ ___
    ☐ Family Income Rider $ ___ for ___ years
    ☐ Home Guardian Rider $ ___ for ___ years
    ☐ Business Guardian Rider $ ___ for ___ years
    ☐ Family Term Rider ☐ One Parent Family Rider $ ___
    ☐ Purchaser Benefit ☐ Death only ☐ Death and Disability
    ☐ Other ___

11. Additional Benefits Applied For
    ☐ Waiver of Premium Benefit
    ☐ Accidental Death Benefit $ ___
    ☐ Guaranteed Insurability Option $ ___
    ☐ Monthly Disability Income $ ___

12. Premium Mode (Minimum premium is $5.00)
    ☐ Annual ☐ Semi-Annual ☐ Quarterly ☐ Monthly
    ☐ Other ___

13. Dividends (if participating)
    ☐ Cash ☐ Reduce Premiums ☐ Paid-up Additions ☐ Accumulate

14. Automatic Premium Loan Provision will be included in policy unless otherwise indicated here ___ ☐ No

351.22 72

Blue Cross Blue Shield of North Carolina
P O BOX 2291
DURHAM, N C 27702

Personal Care Plan
Group Enrollment
Application

PROMPTER

SSUBI _____
SDEPI _____
SADDR _____
RBOSA _____
CNOTE _____

PLEASE PRINT. DO NOT WRITE IN SHADED AREA

RECEIVED DATE

1 SOCIAL SECURITY NUMBER | LAST NAME | FIRST NAME | INITIAL | TITLE (SR MD ETC)

2 MARITAL STATUS

| SINGLE ☐ S | MARRIED ☐ M | SEP ☐ P | WID ☐ W | DIV ☐ D | BIRTHDATE MO DAY YR | BIRTH CENT | SEX ☐ MALE SUB-MSUB ☐ FEMALE SUB-FSUB | MEDICAL SERVICE AREA |

3 RESIDENCE ADDRESS | STREET - RT NO | BOX NO - ETC | CITY | COUNTY | STATE | ZIP

4 **GROUP INFORMATION**

GROUP NUMBER | PACKAGE NUMBER | TYPE OF CONTRACT (*COMPLETE LINES)

☐ EMPLOYEE ONLY | ☐ EMPLOYEE-CHILD* | ☐ FAMILY* | ☐ OTHER*

5 HIRE DATE MO DAY YR | EFFECTIVE DATE MO DAY YR | EMPLOYEE NO (PAYROLL) | DEPARTMENT NO (SECTION) | NPC REF NO

6 NAME OF EMPLOYER OR ORGANIZATION | OCCUPATION

7 **PERSONAL PHYSICIAN**

PERSONAL CARE PHYSICIAN (OR GROUP) NAME | PERSONAL CARE PHYSICIAN (OR GROUP) NUMBER | WERE YOU SEEN BY THIS PHYSICIAN (OR GROUP) BEFORE CHOOSING PERSONAL CARE PLAN COVERAGE?

8 **MEDICARE** ARE YOU ELIGIBLE FOR MEDICARE PART A (HOSPITAL) ☐ YES ☐ NO | EFFECTIVE DATE | DO YOU HAVE MEDICARE PART B (MEDICAL) ☐ YES ☐ NO | EFFECTIVE DATE

9 IS YOUR SPOUSE ELIGIBLE FOR MEDICARE PART A (HOSPITAL) ☐ YES ☐ NO | EFFECTIVE DATE | DOES YOUR SPOUSE HAVE MEDICARE PART B (MEDICAL) ☐ YES ☐ NO | EFFECTIVE DATE

10 **OUT-OF-STATE BLUE CROSS** IF TRANSFERRING FROM OUT-OF-STATE BLUE CROSS OR BLUE SHIELD PLAN, GIVE: | HEADQUARTERS CITY AND STATE OF PLAN | OTHER PLAN'S SUBSCRIBER ID NO | NAME OF SUBSCRIBER

11 **DEPENDENT INFORMATION** LIST SPOUSE AND/OR ELIGIBLE DEPENDENTS TO BE INCLUDED EVERY FAMILY MEMBER MUST SELECT A PERSONAL CARE PHYSICIAN. (OR A GROUP PRACTICE IF THE PHYSICIAN IS WITH A CLINIC) LIST ADDITIONAL CHILDREN ON SEPARATE FORM

| 12 SPOUSE NAME | INITIAL | LAST (IF DIFFERENT) | BIRTHDATE MONTH DAY YEAR | SEX MALE ☐ FEMALE ☐ | | PERSONAL CARE PHYSICIAN (OR GROUP) NAME | PHYSICIAN (GROUP) NO | SEEN BEFORE? ☐ YES ☐ NO |

| 13 FIRST NAME CHILD | INITIAL | LAST (IF DIFFERENT) | BIRTHDATE MONTH DAY YEAR | SEX MALE ☐ FEMALE ☐ | CHILD ☐ | IF AGE 19 OR OVER, STUDENT ☐ HANDICAPPED ☐ | PERSONAL CARE PHYSICIAN (OR GROUP) NAME | PHYSICIAN (GROUP) NO | SEEN BEFORE? ☐ YES ☐ NO |

| 14 FIRST NAME CHILD | INITIAL | LAST (IF DIFFERENT) | BIRTHDATE MONTH DAY YEAR | SEX MALE ☐ FEMALE ☐ | CHILD ☐ | IF AGE 19 OR OVER, STUDENT ☐ HANDICAPPED ☐ | PERSONAL CARE PHYSICIAN (OR GROUP) NAME | PHYSICIAN (GROUP) NO | SEEN BEFORE? ☐ YES ☐ NO |

| 15 FIRST NAME CHILD | INITIAL | LAST (IF DIFFERENT) | BIRTHDATE MONTH DAY YEAR | SEX MALE ☐ FEMALE ☐ | CHILD ☐ | IF AGE 19 OR OVER, STUDENT ☐ HANDICAPPED ☐ | PERSONAL CARE PHYSICIAN (OR GROUP) NAME | PHYSICIAN (GROUP) NO | SEEN BEFORE? ☐ YES ☐ NO |

| 16 FIRST NAME CHILD | INITIAL | LAST (IF DIFFERENT) | BIRTHDATE MONTH DAY YEAR | SEX MALE ☐ FEMALE ☐ | CHILD ☐ | IF AGE 19 OR OVER, STUDENT ☐ HANDICAPPED ☐ | PERSONAL CARE PHYSICIAN (OR GROUP) NAME | PHYSICIAN (GROUP) NO | SEEN BEFORE? ☐ YES ☐ NO |

17 **OTHER INSURANCE** PLEASE COMPLETE IF ANYONE TO BE COVERED IS ALSO COVERED BY ANOTHER GROUP HEALTH INSURANCE POLICY

18 **BLUE CROSS** IF ANYONE TO BE COVERED IS NOW A MEMBER UNDER ANY BLUE CROSS AND BLUE SHIELD OF NORTH CAROLINA CERTIFICATE, GIVE DATA AT RIGHT | SUBSCRIBER ID NO & NAME | DO YOU WANT THE OTHER POLICY TO BE CONTINUED? ☐ YES (DOUBLE COVERAGE) ☐ NO (CANCEL OTHER COVERAGE)

19 **OTHER THAN BLUE CROSS** NAME OF POLICY HOLDER WITH OTHER GROUP INSURANCE | POLICY/CONTRACT NUMBER | EFFECTIVE DATE

NAME AND ADDRESS OF OTHER INSURANCE COMPANY

NAME AND ADDRESS OF EMPLOYER UNDER WHICH THIS COVERAGE IS PROVIDED | IS COVERAGE FOR THE ☐ FAMILY ☐ INDIVIDUAL

20 I certify that all statements made herein are complete and true.

I understand that any coverage provided pursuant to this application shall be subject to the provisions of the certificate and any endorsements thereto which are issued to me by Blue Cross and Blue Shield of North Carolina. Also, I understand that the certificate applied for will not pay benefits for any expenses incurred during the first 12 months after the effective date on account of a disease or physical condition which I now have or have had in the past unless the waiting period is waived under the terms of a master contract or by credit toward the waiting period from another certificate

I hereby authorize all doctors and institutions that have treated or examined me or any person to be covered to release complete medical records and information to Blue Cross and Blue Shield of North Carolina.

21 SIGNATURE OF APPLICANT | DATE SIGNED

A10,2/82 | **PINK COPY SHOULD BE RETAINED BY THE SUBSCRIBER AND USED AS A TEMPORARY ID CARD.**

PERSONAL AUTOMOBILE INSURANCE APPLICATION

☐ Basic Policy
☐ Family Policy

ROYAL-GLOBE INSURANCE ®

PRODUCER NAME		PRODUCER CODE
COMPANY		

APPLICANT'S NAME	OCCUPATION	SOCIAL SECURITY NUMBER

APPLICANT'S ADDRESS (NO., STREET/RFD NO., CITY, STATE, ZIP CODE)	PREVIOUS ADDRESS IF PRESENT ADDRESS LESS THAN 3 YEARS

IF ADDRESS INDICATED IS A P.O. BOX OR RFD, GIVE SPECIFIC DIRECTIONS TO INSURED'S RESIDENCE	POLICY PERIOD From: To: 12:01 AM

DESCRIPTION OF AUTOMOBILE(S) OR TRAILER(S) — TOTAL AUTOMOBILES IN HOUSEHOLD:

CAR		YEAR	MAKE	MODEL	BODY TYPE	CYL.	H.P.	IDENTIFICATION NUMBER	PURCHASED ACTUAL ($) TOTAL COST	MO./YR.	INDICATE LOCATION IF AUTOMOBILE WILL NOT BE PRINCIPALLY GARAGED AT APPLICANT'S ADDRESS:
C	1										
A	2										
	3										
R	4										

NAME AND ADDRESS OF LIENHOLDER (INDICATE CAR NUMBER)	LAST INSTALLMENT DATE OF LOAN

LIST ALL DRIVERS RESIDENT IN HOUSEHOLD — Check applicable boxes:

	NAME (AS SHOWN ON DRIVER'S LICENSE)	DATE OF BIRTH (MO/DAY/YR)	RELATIONSHIP TO APPLICANT	CURRENT DRIVER LICENSE NUMBER (IOWA - SOCIAL SECURITY NUMBER)	NO. YEARS LIC.	DATE OF FIRST LICENSE (MO/DAY/YR)	PERCENTAGE OF USE CAR NUMBER: 1	2	3	4	MALE	FEMALE	MARRIED	IN MILITARY SERVICE	OVER 100 MILES FROM HOME	STUDENT
A.	APPLICANT						%	%	%	%	☐	☐	☐		☐
B.							%	%	%	%	☐	☐	☐		☐
C.							%	%	%	%	☐	☐	☐		☐
D.							100%	100%	100%	100%	☐	☐	☐		☐

**WITHIN THE PRECEDING 40 MONTHS,[1] HAS THE APPLICANT OR ANY OF THE ABOVE NAMED DRIVERS, WHILE OPERATING ANY PRIVATE PASSENGER AUTOMOBILE, BEEN CONVICTED OF A MOVING MOTOR VEHICLE VIOLATION OR BEEN INVOLVED IN AN AUTOMOBILE ACCIDENT RESULTING IN DAMAGE TO ANY PROPERTY OR BODILY INJURY OR DEATH? ☐ YES (EXPLAIN BELOW) ☐ NO

DRIVER SYMBOL (A,B,C,D)	VIOLA-TION	ACCI-DENT	DATE OF VIOLATION OR ACCIDENT (MO/DAY/YR)	BRIEF DESCRIPTION OF ACCIDENT OR VIOLATION (IF SPEEDING, INDICATE RATE AND ZONE)	RESULT OF ACCIDENT BODILY INJ OR DEATH YES NO	DAMAGE TO OWN PROPERTY	DAMAGE TO PROP. OF OTHERS	DATE OF CONVICTION (MO/DAY/YR)	S.D. PTS
	☐	☐			☐ ☐	$	$		
	☐	☐			☐ ☐	$	$		
	☐	☐			☐ ☐	$	$		

HAS APPLICANT OR ANY DRIVER EVER BEEN CONVICTED OF A FELONY OR MISDEMEANOR?
☐ Yes ☐ No Explain:

AGES OF OTHERS IN HOUSEHOLD (INCLUDE ALL CHILDREN)
MALE: FEMALE:

HAS APPLICANT OR ANY DRIVER HAD THEIR DRIVER'S LICENSE SUSPENDED OR REVOKED?
☐ Yes ☐ No
OPERATOR .... From: To:

HAS APPLICANT OR ANY DRIVER: a) ANY PHYSICAL IMPAIRMENT, OR b) EVER BEEN TREATED FOR A MENTAL CONDITION, OR OTHER ILLNESS, SUCH AS HEART AILMENT, EPILEPSY OR DIABETES?
IF "YES" EXPLAIN IN REMARKS AREA   ☐ Yes ☐ No

NAME OF MOST RECENT INSURANCE CARRIER, POLICY NO. AND EXPIRATION DATE:
(IF ASSIGNED RISK IN LAST 4 YEARS, EXPLAIN)

DURING THE PAST 3 YEARS, HAS ANY COMPANY: IF "YES", GIVE SPECIFIC REASON
Cancelled	☐ Yes ☐ No	DOES NOT APPLY IN DISTRICT OF COLUMBIA
Refused to Renew	☐ Yes ☐ No	
Declined	☐ Yes ☐ No	

REMARKS:

I hereby declare to the best of my knowledge and belief that all of the foregoing statements are true and that these statements are offered as an inducement to the company to issue the policy for which I am applying.

DATE OF APPLICATION   **SIGNATURE OF APPLICANT**

I hereby certify to the best of my knowledge and belief that the above is the personal signature of the applicant.

TIME PRODUCER HAS KNOWN APPLICANT   **SIGNATURE OF PRODUCER**

PRODUCER   Initial if coverage is bound _____.

In consideration of the premium to be paid, such coverage as is applied for herein is bound effective from the time and date shown above for the applicant, including the interest of any loss payee to the extent indicated. The insurance afforded by this binder is subject to all of the terms and conditions of the policy and forms applied for. This binder shall terminate upon the effective date of a formal policy issued in replacement hereof or upon valid written notice of cancellation by the company. Notwithstanding anything in the foregoing, this binder shall terminate not later than 12:01 A. M., on the 30th day following the effective date.

UNDERWRITER'S APPROVAL	DATE	DIARY DATE

CL 21613 R   *Submit Good Student App CI 68527
     †Submit Certificate of Completion of approved driver training course.

**Submit required certification for other experience discounts when applicable.
[1]36 Months Applies in District of Columbia

HABITATIONAL BUILDING AND/OR CONTENTS APPLICATION AND UNDERWRITING STATEMENT

HABITATIONAL BUILDING AND/OR CONTENTS APPLICATION AND UNDERWRITING STATEMENT
(IF MORE THAN ONE LOCATION, COMPLETE SEPARATE APPLICATION FOR EACH)

NAME OF COMPANY	DATE	
NAME AND ADDRESS OF APPLICANT OR INSURED		**ATTACH PHOTO AS REQUESTED UNDER "A"**
LOCATION OF RISK (IF OTHER THAN APPLICANT'S OR INSURED'S ADDRESS)		
POLICY NUMBER	IF RENEWAL, GIVE PREVIOUS POLICY NUMBER	
NAME AND ADDRESS OF PRODUCER		

EFFECTIVE DATE	TERM	FORM AND ENDORSEMENT NUMBERS APPLICABLE

AGE (YRS.)
- [ ] 0 to 20
- [ ] 21 to 30
- [ ] 31 to 40
- [ ] Over 40

OCCUPIED BY
- [ ] Owner Only
- [ ] Owner and Tenant
- [ ] Tenant Only

NUMBER OF FAMILIES IN OCCUPANCY
- [ ] One
- [ ] Two
- [ ] Three
- [ ] Four
- [ ] More than four

TYPE OF NEIGHBORHOOD
- [ ] Well to do
- [ ] Middle Income
- [ ] Low Income

HOW LONG HAS PRODUCER KNOWN APPLICANT OR INSURED

INSURANCE CARRIED AND ESTIMATED VALUE

INSURANCE REQUESTED	TOTAL INSURANCE CARRIED	ESTIMATED ACTUAL CASH VALUE OR REPLACEMENT VALUE IF APPLICABLE
BUILDING		
$	$	$
OUTBUILDING		
$	$	$
CONTENTS		
$	$	$

The following questions refer primarily to building characteristics. If coverage is for contents only, answers on building are still required.

    A. *Recent photo must be attached.*
    B. *If one or more answers appear in Column B or there have been any losses within the last five years, please do not issue a policy, but submit for a decision of underwriting acceptability.*

Please use reverse side as required, and for any additional information considered relevant.

	QUESTIONS	COLUMN A	COLUMN B
1.	Exterior Condition	[ ] Excellent [ ] Good	[ ] Fair [ ] Poor
2.	Roof Surface	[ ] Good condition	[ ] Needs repair or resurfacing
3.	Foundation	[ ] Completely enclosed	[ ] Open or partially enclosed
4.	Inside Housekeeping	[ ] Excellent [ ] Good	[ ] Fair [ ] Poor
5.	Heating	[ ] Central heating	[ ] Space heater(s) (Describe type and fuel used on reverse side)
6.	Wiring	[ ] In conduit, sheathed or BX Cable	[ ] Other than described in Column A (Describe on reverse side)
7. Occupancy	a.	[ ] Year Round [ ] Seasonal	[ ] Vacant or Unoccupied
	b.	[ ] Habitational Only	[ ] Other than Habitational (Describe on Reverse Side)
8.	Neighborhood	[ ] Improving [ ] Stable	[ ] Deteriorating
9.	DURING LAST 5 YEARS, HAS ANY COMPANY CANCELLED, REFUSED TO RENEW OR DECLINED INSURANCE ON THIS PROPERTY?	[ ] No	[ ] Yes (Explain on Reverse Side)

CL68928A

Continued on Reverse Side

Form AA-600   (7-70)

COMMONWEALTH OF PENNSYLVANIA
TRAFFIC ACCIDENT REPORT

FORWARD THIS REPORT WITHIN 5 DAYS TO THE PENNSYLVANIA DEPARTMENT OF TRANSPORTATION, BUREAU OF ACCIDENT ANALYSIS, HARRISBURG, PA. 17123

Pennsylvania Vehicle Code, Article XII, Section 1217 states: All reports are confidential, not available as trial evidence

T I M E	Date Of Accident (Month-Day-Year)	Hour		Day Of Week	County
		A.M.	P.M.		

SEVERITY	Estimated Total Damages	$_____	Number Injured_____	Number Killed_____

MY VEHICLE NO 1	Operator's Name (First-Middle-Last)		Sex	Birth (Month-Day-Year)
	Address (Street - City - State)	Zip Code	Operator License No. & State	
	Vehicle Owner's Name (First - Middle - Last)	Vehicle Type (Year - Make - Model)	Estimated Damages	
	Address (Street - City - State)	Zip Code	Vehicle License No. & State	
	Insurance Company		Policy No.	
	Name Of Insured (First - Middle - Last)		Effective Date Of Policy	

VEHICLE NO 2	Operator's Name (First - Middle - Last)		Sex	Birth (Month - Day - Year)
	Address (Street - City - State)	Zip Code	Operator License No. & State	
	Vehicle Owner's Name (First - Middle - Last)	Vehicle Type (Year - Make - Model)	Estimated Damages	
	Address (Street - City - State)	Zip Code	Vehicle License No. & State	

OTHER	Pedestrian's Name (First - Middle - Last)		Sex	Check One
				Not Injured
	Address (Street - City - State)	Zip Code		Injured
				Killed
	Description Of Damaged Property	Property Owner's Name (First - Middle - Last)		
		Estimated Damages	Address (State - City - State)	Zip Code

IF MORE VEHICLES ARE INVOLVED USE EXTRA BLANK PAPER SAME SIZE AS THIS REPORT

POLICE	Name Of Police Dept. Which Investigated Accident
	None

TRAFFIC ACCIDENT REPORT

WEATHER	☐ Rain	☐ Snow	ROADWAY	☐ Wet	☐ Snowy
	☐ Clear	☐ Foggy		☐ Dry	☐ Icy

LOCATION

The Exact Location Of This Accident Will Help Engineers in Efforts To Improve Streets And Highways. Use Official Street Names And Route Numbers Rather Than Locally Used Names. Where Accident Did Not Occur At An Intersection List Careful Measurements To Nearest Landmark.

Accident Occured in (City, Borough, Township)   County)

On (Street Name Or Highway Route No.)   At Intersection With (Street Name Or Highway Route No.)

If Not At Intersection_____ ☐ Feet ☐ Miles   ☐ North   ☐ South   ☐ East   ☐ West   Of

_____ (Cross Street, Highway Route Number, Mile Post, Or Station Number)

INSTRUCTIONS: To properly locate accident use as landmarks, highway station numbers, mile posts, the Intersection of two highways, the names or numbers of bridges, railroad crossings, creeks, streams, city, borough, township or county lines.

Indicate NORTH by arrow

Street or Highway

Street or Highway

Draw Diagram of this Accident as clearly as you can. Write down Streets or Highways. Draw an arrow in the circle so that it points North. Show your Vehicle as Vehicle No. 1.

Place an X in the appropriate box for each vehicle involved in the accident.

Vehicle Type	Veh. No. 1	Veh.No.2
Car		
Car and Trailer		
Truck		
Tractor Trailer		
Bus		
Motorcycle		
Other		

Give a detailed description of accident (Refer to vehicles by number)

Read your complete accident form. If you were not involved could you determine from reading this completed form exactly where and when this accident occurred? Who was involved? What actually happened? If you can answer these questions "yes" you have completed the form well. If your answer to any question is "no" something is missing. Go back and provide the missing information in the appropriate spaces.

Signature _____ Date_____

SWORN STATEMENT
IN PROOF OF LOSS

CLAIM NO.

COMPANY	POLICY SYM. & NO.	POLICY AMOUNT	NAME OF AGENCY

NAME AND ADDRESS OF INSURED	LOCATION OF AGENCY

The above policy insures against loss or damage as described therein according to the terms and conditions of said policy and all forms, endorsements, transfers, and assignments attached thereto.

TIME AND ORIGIN

A loss occurred on _____ 19 ____ at _____ o'clock _____ .M.

The cause and origin of said loss were: _____

_____

_____

OCCUPANCY/USE

The property described was occupied or used at the time of the loss as follows and for no other purpose:

_____

_____

TITLE AND INTEREST

At the time of the loss the interest of your insured in the property described was: _____

_____

and no other person or persons had any interest therein or encumbrance thereon, except _____

_____

CHANGES

Since the policy was issued there has been no assignment thereof, or change of interest, use/occupancy, possession, location or exposure of the property

described except _____

_____

THEFT OR DISAPPEARANCE LOSS

The police authorities at _____ were notified on _____

SUBJECT OF INSURANCE

PROPERTY		AUTOMOBILE
POLICY FORM NUMBER	DATED	DESCRIPTION OF VEHICLE
ITEM 1	ON	TRADE NAME
ITEM 2	ON	TYPE OF BODY
ITEM 3	ON	YEAR AND MODEL
ITEM 4	ON	VEHICLE IDENTIFICATION NUMBER

LOCATION

LOSS IF ANY PAYABLE TO

STATEMENT OF ACTUAL CASH VALUE AND LOSS AND DAMAGE

QUANTITY	PROPERTY	COST OF REPAIR OR REPLACEMENT	DEPRECIATION	ACTUAL CASH VALUE	AMOUNT CLAIMED
TOTALS					

PLATE GLASS REPLACEMENT ESTIMATE

The exact size required to replace the broken plate is _____ X _____

The sizes of salvage are _____ X _____; _____ X _____; _____ X _____; _____ X _____

	ESTIMATE 1	ESTIMATE 2
The cost of replacing glass (at glazer's risk) will be	$ _____	$ _____
Less salvage	$ _____	$ _____
Net amount to be paid by company	$ _____	$ _____

VOTER'S REGISTRATION

NAME		NO.	STREET		WARD	PRECINCT

OCCUPATION	ROOM, APARTMENT FLAT, FLOOR OCCUPIED	POST OFFICE ADDRESS

DATE RESIDENCE IN
ELECTION DISTRICT BEGAN

DESIGNATION OF POLITICAL PARTY FOR PRIMARY VOTE

YEAR	PARTY AFFILIATION	YEAR	PARTY AFFILIATION

PLACE OF LAST   CITY, TOWN OR BOROUGH   STATE
REGISTRATION

NO.   STREET   YEAR

PLACE OF BIRTH   SEX

STATE OR TERRITORY
OF THE UNITED STATES   COLOR
OR FOREIGN COUNTRY

PERSONAL NATURALIZATION

DATE   COURT

PLACE   CERTIFICATE NO.

DERIVATIVE NATURALIZATION

☐ FATHER   ☐ MOTHER   ☐ HUSBAND

STATE OF PENNSYLVANIA   SS:-
COUNTY OF CLINTON
CITY OF LOCK HAVEN

I HEREBY SWEAR OR AFFIRM, THAT ON THE DAY OF THE NEXT ENSUING PRIMARY OR ELECTION, I SHALL HAVE BEEN A CITIZEN OF THE UNITED STATES FOR AT LEAST ONE MONTH, THAT I WILL BE EIGHTEEN YEARS OF AGE, THAT I WILL HAVE RESIDED IN THIS COMMONWEALTH AND IN MY ELECTION DISTRICT FOR AT LEAST THIRTY (30) DAYS, THAT I WILL BE LEGALLY QUALIFIED TO VOTE, THAT I HAVE READ (OR HAVE HAD READ TO ME) THE FOREGOING STATEMENTS MADE IN CONNECTION WITH MY REGISTRATION AND THAT THEY ARE TRUE AND CORRECT.

HIS MARK

SIGNATURE OR MARK OF VOTER

DOES ELECTOR REQUIRE ASSISTANCE TO VOTE?   ☐ YES   ☐ NO

PHYSICAL DISABILITY ☐   IF SO STATE NATURE OF PHYSICAL DISABILITY

ILLITERACY ☐

SUBSCRIBED AND SWORN TO BEFORE

ME THIS_____ DAY OF _____ 19___

HEIGHT	COLOR OF HAIR	COLOR OF EYES	DATE OF BIRTH

SIGNATURE OF REGISTRAR

CITY, BOROUGH, TOWN OR TOWNSHIP OF:
SURNAME (REGISTRAR—DO NOT WRITE BELOW)   CHRISTIAN NAME OR NAMES   SERIAL No **59467**

Signature or mark of Elector

REGISTRATION COMMISSION OF CLINTON COUNTY
CERTIFICATE OF REGISTRATION

Date_____

This certifies that_____

Residing at_____

_____Ward_____District

City
Twp. of_____
Boro.

Has been registered as an elector of the_____
Party of the above district.

Serial No._____ ⬤20   Registrar or Clerk

DEPARTMENT OF STATE
PASSPORT APPLICATION
SEE INSTRUCTIONS—TYPE/PRINT IN INK IN WHITE AREAS

IDENTIFYING INFORMATION

NAME

FIRST/MIDDLE

LAST

MAILING ADDRESS (In Care Of if applicable, Street, City, State, ZIP Code)

R   D   O   DP   Endorsement _____

SEX	PLACE OF BIRTH	DATE OF BIRTH	SOCIAL SECURITY NUMBER

Male   Female   City, State or Province, Country

Month   Day   Year   (Not Mandatory)

HEIGHT   COLOR OF HAIR   COLOR OF EYES   (Area Code) HOME PHONE   (Area Code) BUSINESS PHONE

Feet Inches   PERMANENT ADDRESS (Street, City, State, ZIP Code)   OCCUPATION   DEPARTURE DATE

FATHER'S FULL NAME   FATHER'S BIRTHPLACE AND FATHER'S BIRTH DATE (Mo., Day, Yr.)   FATHER U.S. CITIZEN?   Yes   No

MOTHER'S FULL MAIDEN NAME   MOTHER'S BIRTHPLACE AND MOTHER'S BIRTH DATE (Mo., Day, Yr.)   MOTHER U.S. CITIZEN?   Yes   No

PREVIOUS PASSPORT INFORMATION

HAVE YOU EVER BEEN ISSUED OR INCLUDED IN A U.S. PASSPORT?   Yes   No   IF YES, COMPLETE NEXT LINE REGARDING MOST RECENT PASSPORT. SUBMIT PASSPORT IF AVAILABLE

NAME IN WHICH ISSUED   PASSPORT NUMBER   ISSUE DATE   DISPOSITION OF PASSPORT

Month   Day   Year   (Submitted, Lost, etc.)

MARRIAGE INFORMATION

HAVE YOU EVER BEEN MARRIED?   DATE OF MOST RECENT MARRIAGE   WIFE'S FULL MAIDEN NAME/HUSBAND'S FULL LEGAL NAME

IF YES: Month   Day   Year   TO:

Yes   No

SPOUSE'S PLACE OF BIRTH   SPOUSE'S DATE OF BIRTH   U.S. CITIZEN?   IF WIDOWED/DIVORCED, CHECK BELOW AND GIVE DATE

WIDOWED   DIVORCED

City, State or Province, Country   Month   Day   Year   Yes   No   Month   Day   Year

PROPOSED TRAVEL PLANS AND EMERGENCY ADDRESS (Not Mandatory)

LENGTH OF STAY   COUNTRIES TO BE VISITED

PERSON TO NOTIFY IN CASE OF EMERGENCY ABROAD (Not Traveling With You)

NAME IN FULL

ADDRESS

PHONE NUMBER   RELATIONSHIP

(Area Code)

2" X 2"   FROM 1" TO 1-3/8"

Subscribed and sworn to (affirmed) before me this

_____ Day of _____ 19 ____

DO NOT SIGN APPLICATION UNTIL REQUESTED TO DO SO BY ACCEPTANCE AGENT

I have not, since acquiring United States citizenship, performed any of the acts listed under ''Acts or Conditions'' on the reverse of this application form (unless explanatory statement is attached). I solemnly swear (or affirm) that the statements made on this application are true and the photograph attached is a true likeness of me.

(SEAL)

(To be signed by applicant in presence of acceptance agent)

Postal Employee/
Passport Agent at _____

Clerk of the _____ ,

_____
(Signature of person authorized to accept application)

FOR PASSPORT SERVICES USE ONLY

☐ Birth Cert.   SR   CR   City   ☐ Passport   ☐ Naturalization/Citizenship Cert.

No.:   Filed/Issued: Place: Bearer's Name:

☐ Other:

☐ Seen & Returned   Examiner Name

☐ Attached   Office, Date

FEE _____   EXEC. _____   POST _____

MARRIAGE FORMS

COMMONWEALTH OF PENNSYLVANIA

COUNTY OF CLINTON

MARRIAGE LICENSE APPLICATION

1. COUNTY ISSUING LICENSE CLINTON	**4. OFFICIANT:** **A. NAME**
2. PLACE OF MARRIAGE (CITY, BORO, TOWNSHIP) (COUNTY)	**B. TITLE**
3. DATE OF MARRIAGE (MONTH, DAY, YEAR)	**C. DENOMINATION**

STATEMENT OF MALE	STATEMENT OF FEMALE
5. FULL NAME	**27. FULL NAME**
6. MAILING ADDRESS	**28. MAILING ADDRESS**
7. RESIDENCE **A. STATE** **B. COUNTY** **C. LOCATION** (1) CITY OF _____ (2) BOROUGH OF _____ (3) TOWNSHIP OF	**29. RESIDENCE:** **A. STATE** **B. COUNTY** **C. LOCATION** (1) CITY OF _____ (2) BOROUGH OF _____ (3) TOWNSHIP OF
8. OCCUPATION **9. RACE**	**30. OCCUPATION** **31. RACE**
10. DATE OF BIRTH **11. BIRTHPLACE**	**32. DATE OF BIRTH** **33. BIRTHPLACE**
12A. NUMBER OF PRIOR MARRIAGES **12B. HOW AND WHEN DISSOLVED**	**34A. NUMBER OF PRIOR MARRIAGES** **34B. HOW AND WHEN DISSOLVED**
13. CAUSE(S) IF DIVORCED	**35 CAUSE(S) IF DIVORCED**
14. DOES APPLICANT HAVE ANY TRANSMISSIBLE DISEASE? YES ☐ NO ☐	**36. DOES APPLICANT HAVE ANY TRANSMISSIBLE DISEAES?** YES ☐ NO ☐
15. FATHER'S FULL NAME	**37. FATHER'S FULL NAME**
16. FATHER'S RESIDENCE	**38. FATHER'S RESIDENCE**
17. FATHER'S BIRTHPLACE	**39. FATHER'S BIRTHPLACE**
18. FATHER'S OCCUPATION **19. FATHER'S RACE**	**40. FATHER'S OCCUPATION** **41. FATHER'S RACE**
20. MOTHER'S FULL NAME	**42. MOTHER'S FULL NAME**
21. MOTHER'S MAIDEN NAME	**43. MOTHER'S MAIDEN NAME**
22. MOTHER'S RESIDENCE	**44. MOTHER'S RESIDENCE**
23. MOTHER'S BIRTHPLACE	**45. MOTHER'S BIRTHPLACE**
24. MOTHER'S OCCUPATION **25 MOTHER'S RACE**	**46. MOTHER'S OCCUPATION** **47. MOTHER'S RACE**
26. DOES APPLICANT SATISFY ALL PROVISIONS IN PENNSYLVANIA'S MARRIAGE LAW? (SEE REVERSE SIDE) YES ☐ NO ☐	**48. DOES APPLICANT SATISFY ALL PROVISIONS IN PENNSYLVANIA'S MARRIAGE LAW? (SEE REVERSE SIDE)** YES ☐ NO ☐

WE, THE UNDERSIGNED, EACH OF US DO SOLEMNLY SWEAR THE FACTS SET FORTH ARE TRUE AND CORRECT TO THE BEST OF OUR KNOWLEDGE AND BELIEF AND DO HEREBY MAKE APPLICATION TO THE CLERK OF ORPHANS' COURT OF CLINTON COUNTY, PENNSYLVANIA, FOR LICENSE TO MARRY.

_____   _____
SIGNATURE OF MALE APPLICANT   SIGNATURE OF FEMALE APPLICANT

MARRIAGE FORMS

Consent to the Marriage of a Child or Ward

I, _____ residing

at _____ of _____ do hereby certify

that I am the _____ who is

residing at _____ of the intended marriage of my

now _____ years of age: that I have been informed

said _____ to _____

and hereby consent to the said marriage.

Given before me this _____

day of _____ A.D., 19 _____

_____
Clerk of the Orphans' Court of Clinton County

APPLICATION FOR POST OFFICE BOX

IMPORTANT: Each post office box is rented with the understanding that —

1. Rent is to be paid in advance either quarterly, or for any number of consecutive quarters within the fiscal year, or for a full fiscal year (July 1 — June 30). Failure to pay by the first day of the period due will cause the box to be closed.

2. The box must not be used for any purpose prohibited by postal regulations. Violation of this paragraph shall constitute grounds for closing the box or renewing rental of the box.

3. The use of the box is restricted to one individual, family, firm, or corporation. It may serve only for the delivery of mail addressed in the name of the holder, members of his immediate family, or such members or employees of a firm as may be entitled to receive mail therein. If any of these rules is broken the box may be closed without refund of any part of the rental.

4. The Post Office will furnish one or two regular keys without charge, except if they are not returned when box is surrendered a charge of 50 cents each will be made. A nonrefundable charge of 50 cents will be made for each extra key.

5. Boxholder understands and agrees that all extra or replacement keys shall be obtained from the Postmaster, and under no circumstances will the boxholder or his agent obtain keys for the assigned box from any other source or supplier.

6. The name, address and telephone number of the boxholder contained on Form 1093 may not be disclosed except for law enforcement purposes, in response to a subpoena or court order, or as otherwise specified in Section 261.23h of the Postal Service Manual.

7. The boxholder will furnish a forwarding address at the time he surrenders a lock box or when it is closed for nonpayment of rent.

INSTRUCTIONS FOR WORKING COMBINATION BOX

1. Clear dial by three revolutions to the right, stop on _____
2. Turn dial to the left and stop the second time around on _____
3. Turn right and stop at _____
4. Turn latch key LEFT to open.

Name of person making application (Print or type)

NAME OF FIRM OR CORPORATION (*If box is rented for use of either*)

KIND OF BUSINESS

BUSINESS ADDRESS (*No., street, city, state, and ZIP code*) | TELEPHONE NO.

HOME ADDRESS (*No., street, city, state, and ZIP code*) | TELEPHONE NO.

APPLICANT PLEASE NOTE: Execution of this application signifies your agreement to comply with all postal rules relative to the renting and use of Post Office boxes.

SIGNATURE OF APPLICANT | DATE OF APPLICATION
X |

FOR POST OFFICE USE ONLY	TYPE OF IDENTIFICATION (*Driver's license, military identification, other; show identification number.*)	DATE BOX OPENED	DATE BOX CLOSED	BOX NO.

ADDRESSES VERIFIED BY | TELEPHONE NUMBERS VERIFIED BY

For Post Office Use Only ENTERED IN DIRECTORY	INITIALS OF CLERK	INITIALS OF CARRIER	BOX NO.

THE FOLLOWING MUST BE COMPLETED AND SIGNED BEFORE P.O. BOX IS ASSIGNED

SHOW NAME IN WHICH BOX IS RENTED WHEN OTHER THAN NAME OF APPLICANT

DELIVER MAIL IN ACCORDANCE WITH INSTRUCTIONS CHECKED BELOW

☐ ALL EXCEPT SPECIAL DELIVERY IN BOX
☐ ALL INCLUDING SPECIAL DELIVERY IN BOX
☐ ONLY MAIL ADDRESSED TO BOX IS TO BE PLACED IN IT, ALL OTHER MAIL TO BE DELIVERED AS ADDRESSED.
☐ OTHER INSTRUCTIONS (*Explain*)

SPECIAL DELIVERY MAIL ONLY (*Deliver as checked below*)

☐ DELIVER TO LOCAL RESIDENCE AT
☐ DELIVER TO LOCAL BUSINESS ADDRESS AT

(*No., street, and ZIP code*) | (*No., street, and ZIP code*)

NAMES OF PERSONS ENTITLED TO RECEIVE MAIL THROUGH BOX (*If box is rented to a firm, include the full name of each of its members whose mail is to be placed in box.*)

☐ HAVE READ ITEMS 1 THROUGH 6, ABOVE AND WILL COMPLY WITH THEM.
X _____
(*Signature of applicant*)

PS Form 1093
NOV. 1973

APPLICATION FOR POST OFFICE BOX

CHANGE-OF- ADDRESS FORMS

PS FORM 3573 JUNE 1975

As soon as you know your new address, mail this card to all the people and businesses who send you mail.

Your Name	Print or Type – Last Name, First Name, Middle Initial	New Area Code and Telephone No. if known
Old Address	No. and Street, Apt., Suite, P.O. Box or R.R. No.	
	City, State and ZIP Code	
New Address	No. and Street, Apt., Suite, P.O. Box or R.R. No. (In care of)	
	City, State and ZIP Code	
Sign Here		Date of address change
		Account No. (If any)

PS FORM 3578 JUNE 1975

To make sure you get your magazine or newspaper at your new address promptly, notify the publisher as soon as you know your new address.

If available, paste old label over name and old address sections and complete new address section.

Your Name	Print or Type – Last Name, First Name, Middle Initial	
Old Address	No. and Street, Apt., Suite, P.O. Box or R.R. No.	
	City, State and ZIP Code	Show all Additional Dates and Account Nos. appearing on Address Label
New Address	No. and Street, Apt., Suite, P.O. Box or R.R. No. (In care of)	
	City, State and ZIP Code	
Sign Here		Date of address change

THIS ORDER PROVIDES for the forwarding of First-Class Mail and all parcels of obvious value for a period not to exceed 1 year.	**Print or Type** *(Last Name, First Name, Middle Initial)*
CHANGE OF ADDRESS IS FOR: ☐ **Entire Family** *(When last name of family members differ, separate orders for each last name must be filed.)* ☐ **Individual Signer Only**	**OLD ADDRESS** — No. and St., Apt., Suite, P.O. Box or R.D. No. (In care of)
	Post Office, State and ZIP Code
I AGREE TO PAY FORWARDING POSTAGE FOR NEWSPAPERS AND MAGAZINES FOR 90 DAYS. ☐ NO ☐ YES	**NEW ADDRESS** — No. and St., Apt., Suite, P.O. Box or R.D. No. (In care of)
USPS USE ONLY CLERK/ CARRIER ENDORSEMENT	Post Office, State and ZIP Code
CARRIER ROUTE NUMBER	**Effective Date** — **If Temporary, Expiration Date**
DATE ENTERED	**Sign Here** ▶ — **Date Signed**
	Signature & title of person authorizing address change. (DO NOT print or type.)

CITY OF LOCK HAVEN
DEPARTMENT OF CODE ENFORCEMENT
20 E. Church Street, Lock Haven, Pa. 17745
Telephone 717 - 748-7135

PERMIT NO.

Department of Labor and Industry No.

APPLICATION FOR PLAN EXAMINATION
AND BUILDING PERMIT

IMPORTANT – Applicant to complete all items in sections: I, II, III, IV, and IX.

I. LOCATION OF BUILDING

☐ Borough. ☐ Township ☐ City _____

Subdivision _____

Number and Street _____ Lot _____

Rural Directions _____

(Other local geographic, political, or legal subdivision indentification)

II. TYPE AND COST OF BUILDING – All applicants complete Parts A – D

A. TYPE OF IMPROVEMENT

1 ☐ New building
2 ☐ Addition (If residential, enter number of new housing units added, if any, in Part D, 13)
3 ☐ Alteration (See 2 above)
4 ☐ Repair, replacement
5 ☐ Wrecking (If multifamily residential, enter number of units in building in Part D, 13)
6 ☐ Moving (relocation)
7 ☐ Foundation only

B. OWNERSHIP

8 ☐ Private (individual, corporation, nonprofit institution, etc.)
9 ☐ Public (Federal, State, or local government)

D. PROPOSED USE – For "Wrecking" most recent use

Residential

12 ☐ One family
13 ☐ Two or more family – Enter number of units – – – – → _____
14 ☐ Transient hotel, motel, or dormitory – Enter number of units – – – – – – – → _____
15 ☐ Garage
16 ☐ Carport
17 ☐ Other – Specify _____

_____

_____

Nonresidential

18 ☐ Amusement, recreational
19 ☐ Church, other religious
20 ☐ Industrial
21 ☐ Parking garage
22 ☐ Service station, repair garage
23 ☐ Hospital, institutional
24 ☐ Office, bank, professional
25 ☐ Public utility
26 ☐ School, library, other educational
27 ☐ Stores, mercantile
28 ☐ Tanks, towers
29 ☐ Other – Specify _____

_____

C. COST (Omit cents)

10. Cost of improvement................ $ _____

To be installed but not included in the above cost
a. Electrical...................... _____
b. Plumbing .... _____
c. Heating, air conditioning........ _____
d. Other (elevator, etc.)........... _____

11. TOTAL COST OF IMPROVEMENT $ _____

Nonresidential – Describe in detail proposed use of buildings, e.g., food processing plant, machine shop, laundry building at hospital, elementary school, secondary school, college, parochial school, parking garage for department store, rental office building, office building at industrial plant. If use of existing building is being changed, enter proposed use.

_____

_____

_____

_____

III. SELECTED CHARACTERISTICS OF BUILDING – For new buildings and additions, complete Parts E – L; for wrecking, complete only Part J, for all others skip to IV.

E. PRINCIPAL TYPE OF FRAME

30 ☐ Masonry (wall bearing)
31 ☐ Wood frame
32 ☐ Structural steel
33 ☐ Reinforced concrete
34 ☐ Other – Specify _____

F. PRINCIPAL TYPE OF HEATING FUEL

35 ☐ Gas
36 ☐ Oil
37 ☐ Electricity
38 ☐ Coal
39 ☐ Other – Specify _____

G. TYPE OF SEWAGE DISPOSAL

40 ☐ Public or private company
41 ☐ Private (septic tank, etc.)

H. TYPE OF WATER SUPPLY

42 ☐ Public or private company
43 ☐ Private (well, cistern)

I. TYPE OF MECHANICAL

Will there be central air conditioning?
44 ☐ Yes   45 ☐ No

Will there be an elevator?
46 ☐ Yes   47 ☐ No

J. DIMENSIONS

48. Number of stories................ |____|
49. Total square feet of floor area, all floors, based on exterior dimensions .... |____|
50. Total land area, sq. ft. .... |____|

K. NUMBER OF OFF-STREET PARKING SPACES

51. Enclosed .... |____|
52. Outdoors...................... |____|

L. RESIDENTIAL BUILDINGS ONLY

53. Number of bedrooms .... |____|
54. Number of bathrooms { Full......... |____|
{ Partial....... |____|

MAIL-ORDER FORMS

A Mail-Order Blank (Magazine)

MAIL NO-RISK COUPON TODAY! MONEY-BACK GUARANTEE!

Spencer Gifts C-16 Spencer Bldg., Atlantic City, N.J. 08411
Bringing You Direct Mail Savings For Over 25 Years.

YES! Please rush my giant personalized Wall Calendar. Enclosed is color print or slide which will be returned to me in perfect condition. I understand that I must be delighted or I may return everything for a full cash refund.

No. of Calendars (circle number)	1	2	4	8
Full Color P-81109	$4.99	$8.99	$16.99	$32.99
Black & White P-53751	$3.99	$6.99	$12.99	$24.99
Postage & Handling	.35	.50	.75	$1.00

On the back of your photo, print the name you want to appear on your photo calendar.

Please Print:
NAME__________
ADDRESS__________
CITY__________
STATE__________ZIP______

Cost of Calendar(s) Ordered $______
Add Postage & Handling $______
Add State Tax (see chart) $______
Enclosed is ☐ check or ☐ money order for Total $______

STATE SALES TAX CHART Find your State & add the Sales Tax in the space on the coupon NE 2½ %, OH, UT 4½%; NYC 8%, CA PA 6% CT, NY 7%, AR, CO, GA, IA, KS, LA, MA OK 3%, AZ FL IL, IN MD, MI, MN, MO, NC, SC 4% WI VA 4%, AL KY ME, NJ, RI, TN, TX 5%

B Mail-Order Blank (Catalog)

JCPenney

IS THIS YOUR FIRST ORDER FROM ANY PENNEY CATALOG? ☐ YES ☐ NO DATE______19___

PLEASE PRINT YOUR PENNEY CUSTOMER NUMBER HERE ☐☐☐-☐☐☐-☐☐☐-☐-☐

MAIL THIS ORDER TO:

J. C. Penney
90 Annex
Atlanta,
Ga. 30390

OR

J. C. Penney
Catalog Div.
11800 W. Burleigh St.
Milwaukee, Wis. 53263

FOREIGN ☐ S/B ☐ T.E. ☐

Please PRINT and use same name for ALL orders from your household
NAME__________ (First name) (Middle Initial) (Last name)
Please print your Husband's or Wife's first name and middle initial__________
ADDRESS__________ (R.R.) (R.R. Box) (P.O. Box)
CITY______STATE______ZIP______
TELEPHONE NO.______ (Area Code) ______ (Telephone Number)

If your NAME AND/OR ADDRESS HAS CHANGED since your last order, please PRINT former name and address here
NAME__________
ADDRESS__________
CITY__________
STATE______ZIP______

SHIP TO ANOTHER ADDRESS? If you want this order shipped to another person or to a different address, PRINT DIRECTIONS HERE: C/M
NAME__________
ADDRESS__________ (R.R.) (R.R. Box) (P.O. Box)
CITY______STATE______ZIP______

PLEASE list TIME PAYMENT purchases on a separate Order Form—DO NOT ENCLOSE Credit payments with this order.

Page No.	Name of Item	How many (Pkgs., etc.) do you want?	Catalog Number			Size (Measure to be sure)	Color, Pattern, Finish, Style, etc.		Price for one (Pkg., Yd., Ea., etc.)	Total Price	Cash Orders Fill in Mailing Weights
			Letter	Numbers	Ltr.(s)		No. or Code	Name			

CREDIT ORDER

NOTE: Check only one. Do not combine Time Payment with Regular Charge Account or Cash purchases on one order form.

☐ **NEW ACCOUNT**–To apply for credit: (1) Fill out the application on page 736 or 738. (2) SIGN the Charge Account Agreement on page 739 and send with your order. (3) *Also*, SIGN the following agreement: I agree to pay the credit price for this order in accordance with my Regular Charge Account Agreement.

*SIGNATURE*__________

☐ **REGULAR CHARGE ACCOUNT**–If you have a Charge Account, please SIGN this agreement: I agree to pay the credit price for this order in accordance with my Regular Charge Account Agreement.
*SIGNATURE*__________

☐ **TIME PAYMENT ACCOUNT**–If you have a Penney Charge Account, READ and SIGN the Time Payment Account Agreement on page 740. Mail the signed Agreement with your order. Only items listed on page 741 of our Fall Catalog may be charged to this account.

Fill in Spaces Below If This Is a CASH Order

CHK | MO | CS | O

1. MERCHANDISE TOTAL		Add mailing weights and write total here.
2. AMOUNT FOR SALES TAXES (see page 730)		
3. AMOUNT FOR PARCEL POST CHARGE*		Write here the Parcel Post charge for the above weight. Find it in the Rate Chart on page 732.
TOTAL AMOUNT OF ORDER		
4. INCLUDE AMOUNT DUE (If any) FROM A PREVIOUS CASH ORDER		
CASH AMOUNT ENCLOSED (total of 1, 2, 3, 4 above)		

PAY BY CHECK OR MONEY ORDER ONLY. DO NOT SEND STAMPS OR CURRENCY. WE **CANNOT ACCEPT** C.O.D. ORDERS. **DO NOT** ENCLOSE CREDIT ACCOUNT PAYMENTS.

*HOW WE SHIP—We ship by Parcel Post whenever possible; REA-Express or Truck are used for orders containing not-mailable merchandise, and orders exceeding Parcel Post weight and size limits. See page 730 for details. Depend on us to ship the best way.

R-73 JCPenney 737

Department of the Treasury — Internal Revenue Service

1982 Form 1040A US Individual Income Tax Return (O)

OMB No. 1545-0085

Step 1
Name and address

Use the IRS mailing label. Otherwise, print or type.

Your first name and initial (if joint return, also give spouse's name and initial) Last name Your social security no.

Present home address Spouse's social security no.

City, town or post office, State, and ZIP code Your occupation

Spouse's occupation

Presidential Election Campaign Fund

Do you want $1 to go to this fund?. . . . . ☐ Yes ☐ No

If joint return, does your spouse want $1 to go to this fund? ☐ Yes ☐ No

Step 2
Filing status
(Check only one)
and Exemptions

Attach Copy B of Forms W-2 here

1 ☐ Single (See if you can use Form 1040EZ.)

2 ☐ Married filing joint return (even if only one had income)

3 ☐ Married filing separate return. Enter spouse's social security no. above and full name here. _____

4 ☐ Head of household (with qualifying person). If the qualifying person is your unmarried child but not your dependent, write this child's name here. _____

Always check the exemption box labeled Yourself. Check other boxes if they apply.

5a ☐ Yourself ☐ 65 or over ☐ Blind

  b ☐ Spouse ☐ 65 or over ☐ Blind

Write number of boxes checked on 5a and b ☐

  c First names of your dependent children who lived with you _____

Write number of children listed on 5c ☐

  d Other dependents:

(1) Name	(2) Relationship	(3) Number of months lived in your home.	(4) Did dependent have income of $1,000 or more?	(5) Did you provide more than one-half of dependent's support?

Write number of other dependents listed on 5d ☐

  e Total number of exemptions claimed . . . .

Add numbers entered in boxes above ☐

Step 3
Adjusted gross income

6 Wages, salaries, tips, etc. *(Attach Forms W-2)*. . . . . 6 _____ .

7 Interest income *(Complete page 2 if over $400 or you have any All-Savers interest)*. . . . . . 7 _____

8a Dividends _____ . (Complete page 2 if over $400) 8b Exclusion _____ . Subtract line 8b from 8a 8c

9a Unemployment compensation (insurance). Total from Form(s) 1099-UC _____ .

  b Taxable amount, if any, from worksheet on page 16 of Instructions. 9b

10 Add lines 6, 7, 8c, and 9b. This is your total income. 10

11 Deduction for a married couple when both work. Complete the worksheet on page 17. 11

12 Subtract line 11 from line 10. This is your adjusted gross income. 12

Step 4
Taxable income

13 Allowable part of your charitable contributions. Complete the worksheet on page 18. 13

14 Subtract line 13 from line 12. 14

15 Multiply $1,000 by the total number of exemptions claimed in box 5e. 15

16 Subtract line 15 from line 14. This is your taxable income. 16

Step 5
Tax, credits, and payments

Attach check or money order here

17a Partial credit for political contributions. See page 19. . . . . . . ■ 17a

  b Total Federal income tax withheld, from W-2 form(s). *(If line 6 is more than $32,400, see page 19.)*. . . . . 17b _____ .

Stop Here and Sign Below if You Want IRS to Figure Your Tax

  c Earned income credit, from worksheet on page 21. . . . . 17c _____ .

18 Add lines 17a, b, and c. These are your total credits and payments. . . . . . . 18 _____ .

19a Find tax on amount on line 16. Use tax table, pages 26-31. . . . . 19a _____ .

  b Advance EIC payment *(from W-2 form(s))*. . . . . 19b _____

20 Add lines 19a and 19b. This is your total tax. 20

Step 6
Refund or amount you owe

21 If line 18 is larger than line 20, subtract line 20 from line 18. Enter the amount to be **refunded to you**. 21

22 If line 20 is larger than line 18, subtract line 18 from line 20. Enter the **amount you owe.** Attach payment for full amount payable to "Internal Revenue Service." 22

Step 7
Sign your return

I have read this return and any attachments filed with it. Under penalties of perjury, I declare that to the best of my knowledge and belief, the return and attachments are correct and complete.

▶ Your signature Date ▶ Spouse's signature (If filing jointly, BOTH must sign)

Paid preparer's signature Date Check if self-employed ☐ Preparer's social security no.

Firm's name (or yours, if self-employed) E.I. no.

Address and Zip code

For **Privacy Act and Paperwork Reduction Act Notice,** see page 34.

FEDERAL BUREAU OF INVESTIGATION
UNITED STATES DEPARTMENT OF JUSTICE
WASHINGTON, D.C. 20537

APPLICANT

1. LOOP

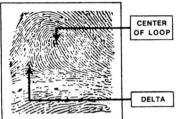

CENTER OF LOOP

DELTA

THE LINES BETWEEN CENTER OF LOOP AND DELTA MUST SHOW

2. WHORL

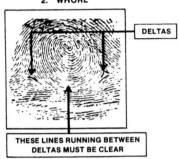

DELTAS

THESE LINES RUNNING BETWEEN DELTAS MUST BE CLEAR

3. ARCH

ARCHES HAVE NO DELTAS

TO OBTAIN CLASSIFIABLE FINGERPRINTS:

1. USE PRINTER'S INK.
2. DISTRIBUTE INK EVENLY ON INKING SLAB.
3. WASH AND DRY FINGERS THOROUGHLY.
4. ROLL FINGERS FROM NAIL TO NAIL, AND AVOID ALLOWING FINGERS TO SLIP.
5. BE SURE IMPRESSIONS ARE RECORDED IN CORRECT ORDER.
6. IF AN AMPUTATION OR DEFORMITY MAKES IT IMPOSSIBLE TO PRINT A FINGER, MAKE A NOTATION TO THAT EFFECT IN THE INDIVIDUAL FINGER BLOCK.
7. IF SOME PHYSICAL CONDITION MAKES IT IMPOSSIBLE TO OBTAIN PERFECT IMPRESSIONS, SUBMIT THE BEST THAT CAN BE OBTAINED WITH A MEMO STAPLED TO THE CARD EXPLAINING THE CIRCUMSTANCES.
8. EXAMINE THE COMPLETED PRINTS TO SEE IF THEY CAN BE CLASSIFIED, BEARING IN MIND THAT MOST FINGERPRINTS FALL INTO THE PATTERNS SHOWN ON THIS CARD (OTHER PATTERNS OCCUR INFREQUENTLY AND ARE NOT SHOWN HERE).

LEAVE THIS SPACE BLANK

THIS CARD FOR USE BY:

1. LAW ENFORCEMENT AGENCIES IN FINGERPRINTING APPLICANTS FOR LAW ENFORCEMENT POSITIONS, AND APPLICANTS FOR EMPLOYMENT LICENSES OR PERMITS IN THOSE STATES WITH STATUTES PROVIDING FOR FINGERPRINTING AS A REQUISITE FOR THE TYPE OF EMPLOYMENT, LICENSE OR PERMIT TO BE ISSUED. LOCAL AND COUNTY ORDINANCES, UNLESS SPECIFICALLY BASED ON APPLICABLE STATE STATUTES, DO NOT SATISFY THIS REQUIREMENT. A SET OF APPLICANT PRINTS MUST FIRST BE CHECKED THROUGH THE APPROPRIATE STATE IDENTIFICATION BUREAU OR, IF NO SUCH BUREAU EXISTS, THROUGH A CENTRAL AGENCY DESIGNATED FOR SUCH PURPOSE WITHIN THE STATE. ONLY THOSE FINGERPRINTS FOR WHICH NO DISQUALIFYING RECORD HAS BEEN FOUND LOCALLY SHOULD BE SUBMITTED FOR FBI SEARCH. IF A MORE CURRENT COPY OF AN EXISTING FBI IDENTIFICATION RECORD IS REQUIRED, SIMPLY SUPPLY NAME, FBI NUMBER OR LOCAL ARREST NUMBER AND, IF READILY AVAILABLE, THE PRIMARY AND SECONDARY PARTS OF THE FINGERPRINT CLASSIFICATION.

2. U.S. GOVERNMENT AGENCIES IN CONNECTION WITH CLEARANCES, IDENTITY OF PRIVATE CONTRACTOR SHOULD BE SHOWN IN SPACE "EMPLOYER AND ADDRESS." THE CONTRIBUTOR IS THE NAME OF AGENCY SUBMITTING THE FINGERPRINT CARD TO THE FBI.

FBI NUMBER, IF KNOWN, SHOULD ALWAYS BE FURNISHED IN APPROPRIATE SPACE.

MISCELLANEOUS NO. - RECORD: OTHER ARMED FORCES NO., PASSPORT NO. (PP), ALIEN REGISTRATION NO. (AR), PORT SECURITY CARD NO. (PS), SELECTIVE SERVICE NO. (SS), VETERANS' ADMINISTRATION CLAIM NO. (VA).

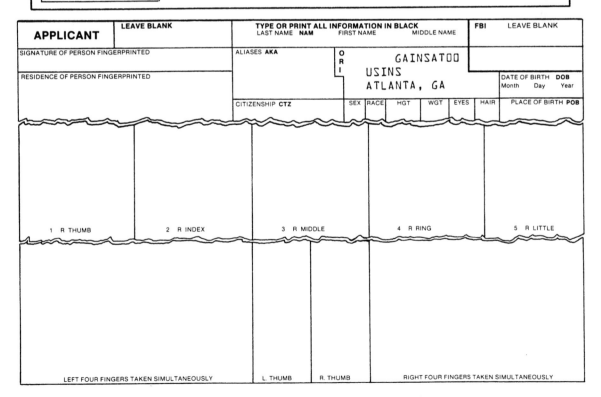

NORTH CAROLINA DEPARTMENT OF HUMAN RESOURCES
Division of Social Services

DSS-1698 (Rev. 6-80)
Food Assistance
(DSS-FS-1)

APPLICATION FOR FOOD STAMPS - PART 1

For Office Use Only

Case number _____

Date received _____

Step 1. Complete Page 1

To begin to apply for food stamps, you can complete this first page, tear it off and give it to us. We are required to take action on your application within 30 days from the date you give us this first page. So, the sooner you give us the first page, the quicker you will know whether you will receive food stamps. Now go to Step 2.

Step 2. Complete Pages 2-5

Pages 2-5 must be completed before we can see if you're eligible for food stamps. You can return pages 2-5 to us along with the first page or at the time of the interview we will schedule for you. Try to fill out as much as possible now. Your case worker will help you with the rest during the interview.

Your name _____

Telephone number where you can be reached _____

Mailing Address _____ City _____ State _____ Zip Code _____

If you don't have a street address, tell us how to get to your home.

Sign here _____

Today's date _____

If You Need Food Stamps Right Away

If your household (you and the people who live and eat with you) has little or no income right now, you may be able to receive food stamps within a few days. Answer the following questions only if your household has little or no income and needs food stamps right away.

Has anyone in your household received any income so far this month?

☐ Yes   ☐ No   If yes, how much? $

Did your household's only income recently stop?

☐ Yes   ☐ No

Does anyone in your household expect to receive income later this month?

☐ Yes   ☐ No   ☐ Don't know   If yes, how much? $ _____ When?

How many people live in your home and eat with you? (Include yourself)

Is anyone in your household 60 years or older?

☐ Yes   ☐ No

Is anyone in your household receiving Supplemental Security Income (SSI) benefits or Social Security Disability Payments?

☐ Yes   ☐ No

How much do the members of your household have in cash and savings? (Give your best estimate of the total,)

$

Answer the following questions honestly and completely. If you know but refuse on purpose to give any needed information, your household (you and the people who live and eat with you) won't be eligible for food stamps.

You may complete this form at home and mail it or bring it to the food stamps office. Or, another member of your household, or an adult who knows you may complete and return it to us.

Important: When you are interviewed, please bring proof of all household income – for example pay stubs and award letters for government benefits (such as SSI or Social Security). We may also need the following items: statements of all household savings and checking accounts; rent or mortgage receipts; and utility bills

Having these items with you could speed up your application.

Your name _____

Telephone number where you can be reached _____

Mailing Address _____ City _____ State _____ Zip Code _____

If you don't have a street address, tell us how to get to your home.

Household Members

Fill in all blanks for each household member, including yourself. People who live and eat with you (except roomers or boarders) should be listed as household members. For each person who is not a citizen, you will need to show the food stamp office an alien registration card, such as INS Forms I-151, I-551, I-94, or a Re-entry Permit.

The submission of the Social Security number (SSN) for all household members 18 years and over and those children under 18 years with countable income is mandatory under the Food Stamp

Act of 1977 as amended by PL 96-58 (7 U.S.C. 2025 F). Your SSN will be used in the administration of the food stamp program to check the identity of household members, prevent duplicate participation and to facilitate making mass changes. Your SSN will also be used in computer matching and program reviews or audits to make sure your household is eligible for food stamps. This may result in criminal or civil action or administrative claims against persons fraudulently participating in the Food Stamp Program

Name	Age	Social security number	Is this person a U.S. citizen?
1			☐ Yes ☐ No

2 _____ | | .... ☐ Yes ☐ No

3 _____ | | .... ☐ Yes ☐ No

4 _____ | | .... ☐ Yes ☐ No

Resources

Does anyone in your household own any cars, trucks, boats, campers, motorcycles or other vehicles?		Make	Model	Year
☐ Yes ☐ No If yes, please describe.	1			

Make	Model	Year	Make	Model	Year
2			3		

Does your household have any savings?	Cash on hand	Savings account/ Credit Union	Checking Account	Stocks, Bonds, Other
☐ Yes ☐ No If yes, how much?	$	$	$	$

Does your household own any real estate *other than your* home? For example, land or buildings, including buildings you rent to others.
☐ Yes ☐ No

If yes, you may need to bring information about the value of the property, any property, any amount owed, and how the property is used.

Did you or a member of your household sell, trade or give away anything of substantial value during the last three months?
☐ Yes ☐ No

Income from Work

Fill in all blanks for each household member with a full or part-time job. If a member has more than one job, list each job separately.

Include members who receive income from CETA or WIN. Do not include self-employed household members.

Household member	Name of employer	Amount of each pay check *before* deductions such as taxes, retirement, or union dues are taken out	How often paid
1		$	
2		$	
3		$	

Is anyone in your household self-employed?

☐ Yes ☐ No If yes, give their names

Please bring last year's Federal Tax forms for *self-employed* members of your household. Or, if no such tax forms were filed last year, bring proof of self-employment costs and income.

Has anyone in your household quit a job in the last 60 days? ☐ Yes ☐ No

Other Income Amounts

Source of income	Household members who receive this income	Amount of each check or payment	How often received
AFDC (Aid to Families with Dependent Children)	1	$	
	2	$	
Social Security -- Blue/green checks	1	$	
	2	$	
SSI (Supplemental Security Income)–Gold checks	1	$	
	2	$	
GA (general assistance)	1	$	
	2	$	
VA (Veterans benefits)	1	$	
Pensions or retirement income	1	$	
	2	$	
Unemployment or Workers' Compensation	1	$	
	2	$	
Child support and alimony	1	$	
	2	$	
Money from friends or relatives (other than loans)	1	$	
Other (specify)	1	$	
	2	$	

UNITED STATES DEPARTMENT OF JUSTICE
IMMIGRATION AND NATURALIZATION SERVICE

OMB NO. 1115–0009
Approval Expires 1/31/84

FEE STAMP

APPLICATION TO FILE PETITION FOR NATURALIZATION

Mail or take to:

IMMIGRATION AND NATURALIZATION SERVICE

(See INSTRUCTIONS. BE SURE YOU UNDERSTAND EACH QUESTION BEFORE YOU ANSWER IT. PLEASE PRINT OR TYPE.)

ALIEN REGISTRATION
(Show the exact spelling of your name as it appears on your alien registration receipt card, and the number of your card. If you did not register, so state.)

Name ....

No. ....

Section of Law .... (Leave Blank)

Date: ....

(1) My full true and correct name is.. (Full true name without abbreviations)

(2) I now live at.. (Number and street,)

(City, county, state, zip code)

(3) I was born on.. (Month) (Day) (Year) in........................ (City or town) (County, province, or state) (Country)

(4) I request that my name be changed to..

(5) Other names I have used are: .... (Include maiden name)   Sex: ☐ Male   ☐ Female

(6) Was your father or mother ever a United States citizen?.. ☐ Yes ☐ No
(If "Yes", explain fully)

(7) Can you read and write English?.. ☐ Yes ☐ No

(8) Can you speak English?.. ☐ Yes ☐ No

(9) Can you sign your name in English?.. ☐ Yes ☐ No

(10) My lawful admission for permanent residence was on.. (Month) (Day) (Year) ....under the name of
.... at.. (City) (State)

(11) (a) I have resided continuously in the United States since .... (Month) (Day) (Year)

(b) I have resided continuously in the State of .... since .... (Month) (Day) (Year)

(c) During the last five years I have been physically in the United States for a total of .... months.

From -	To -	Street Address	City and State
(a) ...., 19........	Present Time		
(b) ...., 19........	............., 19........		
(c) ...., 19........	............., 19........		
(d) ...., 19........	............., 19........		

(14) (a) Have you been out of the United States since your lawful admission as a permanent resident?.. ☐ Yes ☐ No
If "Yes" fill in the following information for every absence of *less than 6 months*, no matter how short it was.

Date Departed	Date Returned	Name of Ship, or of Airline, Railroad Company, Bus Company, or Other Means Used to Return to the United States	Place or Port of Entry Through Which You Returned to the United States

(b) Since your lawful admission, have you been out of the United States for a period of *6 months or longer?*.. ☐ Yes ☐ No
If "No", state "None"; If "Yes", fill in following information for every absence of more than 6 months.

Date Departed	Date Returned	Name of Ship or of Airline, Railroad Company, Bus Company, or Other Means Used to Return to the United States	Place or Port of Entry Through Which You Returned to the United States

NAME_____ DATE _____

(15) The law provides that you may not be regarded as qualified for naturalization, if you knowingly committed certain offenses or crimes, even though you may not have been arrested. Have you ever, in or outside the United States:

    (a) knowingly committed any crime for which you have not been arrested?.................................☐ Yes ☐ No

    (b) been arrested, cited, charged, indicted, convicted, fined or imprisoned for breaking or violating any law or ordinance, including traffic regulations?...☐ Yes ☐ No

If you answer "Yes" to (a) or (b), give the following information as to each incident.

	WHEN	WHERE	(City)	(State)	(Country)	NATURE OF OFFENSE	OUTCOME OF CASE, IF ANY
(a)							
(b)							
(c)							
(d)							
(e)							

(16) List your present and past membership in or affiliation with every organization, association, fund, foundation, party, club, society or similar group in the United States or in any other country or place, and your foreign military service. (If none, write "None.")

(a)		, 19........	to 19........
(b)		, 19........	to 19........
(c)		, 19........	to 19........
(d)		, 19........	to 19........
(e)		, 19........	to 19........
(f)		, 19........	to 19........
(g)		, 19........	to 19........

(17) (a) Are you now, or have you ever, in the United States or in any other place, been a member of, or in any other way connected or associated with the Communist Party? (If "Yes", attach full explanation) ....☐ Yes ☐ No

    (b) Have you ever knowingly aided or supported the Communist Party directly, or indirectly through another organization, group or person? (If "Yes", attach full explanation) ....☐ Yes ☐ No

    (c) Do you now or have you ever advocated, taught, believed in, or knowingly supported or furthered the interests of Communism? (If "Yes", attach full explanation) ....☐ Yes ☐ No

(18) During the period March 23, 1933 to May 8, 1945, did you serve in, or were you in any affiliated with, either directly or indirectly, any military unit, paramilitary unit, police unit, self-defense unit, vigilante unit, citizen unit, unit of the Nazi Party or SS, government agency or office, extermination camp, concentration camp, prisoner of war camp, prison, labor camp, detention camp or transit camp, under the control of or affiliated with:

    (a) the Nazi Government of Germany ....☐ Yes ☐ No

    (b) any Government in any area occupied by, allied with, or established with the assistance or cooperation of, the Nazi Government of Germany? ....☐ Yes ☐ No

(19) During the period March 23, 1933 to May 8, 1945, did you ever order, incite, assist, or otherwise participate in the persecution of any person because of race, religion, national origin, or political opinion?...........................☐ Yes ☐ No

(20) Have you borne any hereditary title or have you been of any order of nobility in any foreign state? ....☐ Yes ☐ No

(21) Have you ever been declared legally incompetent or have you ever been confined as a patient in a mental institution? ....☐ Yes ☐ No

(22) Are deportation proceedings pending against you, or have you ever been deported or ordered deported, or have you ever applied for suspension of deportation? ....☐ Yes ☐ No

(23) (a) My last Federal income tax return was filed........................... (year) Do you owe any Federal taxes? ....☐ Yes ☐ No

    (b) Since becoming a permanent resident of the United States, have you:

      —filed an income tax return as a nonresident? ....☐ Yes ☐ No

      —failed to file an income tax return because you regarded yourself as a nonresident? ....☐ Yes ☐ No

    (If you answer "Yes" to (a) or (b) explain fully.)

(24) Have you ever claimed in writing, or in any other way, to be a United States citizen? ....☐ Yes ☐ No

(25) (a) Have you ever deserted from the military, air, or naval forces of the United States? ....☐ Yes ☐ No

    (b) If male, have you ever left the United States to avoid being drafted into the Armed Forces of the United States? ......☐ Yes ☐ No

(26) The law provides that you may not be regarded as qualified for naturalization if, at *any* time during the period for which you are required to prove good moral character, you have been a habitual drunkard; committed adultery; advocated or practiced polygamy; have been a prostitute or procured anyone for prostitution; have knowingly and for gain helped any alien to enter the United States illegally; have been an illicit trafficker in narcotic drugs or marijuana; have received your income mostly from illegal gambling, or have given false testimony for the purpose of obtaining any benefits under this Act. Have you ever, *anywhere*, been such a person or committed any of these acts? (If you answer yes to any of these, attach full explanation.) ....☐ Yes ☐ No

(27) Do you believe in the Constitution and form of government of the United States? ....☐ Yes ☐ No

(28) Are you willing to take the full oath of allegiance to the United States? (See Instructions) ....☐ Yes ☐ No

(29) If the law requires it, are you willing:

    (a) to bear arms on behalf of the United States? (If "No", attach full explanation) ....☐ Yes ☐ No

    (b) to perform noncombatant services in the Armed Forces of the United States? (If "No", attach full explanation) ....☐ Yes ☐ No

    (c) to perform work of national importance under civilian direction? (If "No"', attach full explanation) ....☐ Yes ☐ No

(30) (a) If male, did you ever register under United States Selective Service laws or draft laws? ....☐ Yes ☐ No

    If "Yes" give date...............; Selective Service No.....................; Local Board No...............; Present classification...............

    (b) Did you ever apply for exemption from military service because of alienage, conscientious objections, or other reasons? ☐ Yes ☐ No

    If "Yes," explain fully...

⊔⊔ ⊔⊔ western union

Telegram

MSG. NO	NO. WDS. CL. OF SVC.	PD.—COLL.	CASH NO.	ACCOUNTING INFORMATION	DATE	FILING TIME	SENT TIME
MAY	2006					A.M. P.M.	A.M. P.M.

Send the following message, subject to the terms
on back hereof, which are hereby agreed to.

☐ OVERNIGHT TELEGRAM
UNLESS BOX ABOVE IS CHECKED THIS
MESSAGE WILL BE SENT AS A TELEGRAM

CARE OF
OR APT. NO.

TO

ADDRESS & TELEPHONE NO.

CITY — STATE & ZIP CODE

SENDER'S TEL. NO.   **NAME & ADDRESS**

OFFICE USE ONLY

EOM

(BILL TO) / (ADDRESS) / (CITY - STATE - ZIP) / (CHG. METH.)

X-OFF

(CHG.#) / (OPR.#) / (HF) / (PC CODE) / (PC AMT.) / (GIFT AMT.) / (TAX) / (AGT. I.D.) / (SG)

⊔⊔ ⊔⊔ western union AGENCY MONEY ORDER PAYMENT AUTHORIZATION

Identifying Number ❯	Originating Office ❯		Date ❯	Time Filed ❯

Money Order Control No. (MOD No.) | | | | | | | | | | | | ← Must Be 10 Digits   CNT ☐   CPT ☐

Pay Amount _____ ($ _____ . ____)
(PRINT AMOUNT IN DOLLARS AND CENTS)   (FIGURES)

Pay To _____   Test Question _____

Address _____   City - State _____

Sender's Name _____   Date/Time Received _____

Control Office Verification _____   Date/Time Payee Notified _____   Date/Time Paid _____
(OPR No. or Initials)

⌈ Draft No. _____
When preparing Draft – the 10 digit Money Order
Control No. (MOD No.) must be included. ⌉

Payee Identification _____

⊔⊔ ⊔⊔ western union

The Money Order Includes the Following Message: